Mr. Big

The Investigation into the Deaths of Karen and Krista Hart

Mr. Big

THE INVESTIGATION INTO THE DEATHS OF KAREN AND KRISTA HART

Colleen Lewis and Jennifer Hicks

FLANKER PRESS LIMITED
ST. JOHN'S

Library and Archives Canada Cataloguing in Publication

Lewis, Colleen, 1971-, author
    Mr. Big : the investigation into the deaths of Karen and Krista Hart
/ Colleen Lewis and Jennifer Hicks.

Issued in print and electronic formats.
ISBN 978-1-77117-431-2 (paperback).--ISBN 978-1-77117-432-9 (html).--
ISBN 978-1-77117-433-6 (kindle).--ISBN 978-1-77117-434-3 (pdf)

    1. Undercover operations--Newfoundland and Labrador. 2. Hart,
Nelson--Trials, litigation, etc. 3. Filicide--Newfoundland and Labrador.
4. Hicks, Jennifer, 1974-. 5. Abused women--Newfoundland and
Labrador--Biography. I. Hicks, Jennifer, 1974-, author II. Title.

HV8080.U5L49 2015   363.2'32   C2015-905577-6
                                                                 C2015-905578-4

© 2015 by Colleen Lewis and Jennifer Hicks

PRINTED IN CANADA

RECYCLED
Paper made from
recycled material
FSC
www.fsc.org   FSC® C103567

This paper has been certified to meet the environ-
mental and social standards of the Forest Stewardship
Council® (FSC®) and comes from responsibly managed forests, and verified recycled sources.

Cover Design by Graham Blair

FLANKER PRESS LTD.
PO BOX 2522, STATION C
ST. JOHN'S, NL
CANADA

TELEPHONE: (709) 739-4477   FAX: (709) 739-4420   TOLL-FREE: 1-866-739-4420
WWW.FLANKERPRESS.COM

9 8 7 6 5 4 3 2

        Canada Council   Conseil des Arts
for the Arts   du Canada

We acknowledge the [financial] support of the Government of Canada. *Nous reconnaissons l'appui [financier] du gouvernement
du Canada*. We acknowledge the support of the Canada Council for the Arts, which last year invested $153 million to bring
the arts to Canadians throughout the country. *Nous remercions le Conseil des arts du Canada de son soutien. L'an dernier, le
Conseil a investi 153 millions de dollars pour mettre de l'art dans la vie des Canadiennes et des Canadiens de tout le pays*. We
acknowledge the financial support of the Government of Newfoundland and Labrador, Department of Tourism, Culture and
Recreation for our publishing activities.

Dedicated to the memory
of Karen and Krista Hart

These are the events according to Jennifer Hicks,
as written by Colleen Lewis.

The little dark-haired fourteen year-old is looking forward to getting home this afternoon. Her father is there, waiting. And when her homework is completed, the pair will set out on an adventure that will keep them busy to nearly midnight.

Jennifer Hicks is the youngest of four daughters. Her mother, Gertrude, is the breadwinner of the family. She is a home care worker who works night shifts.

Her father, Cyril, can no longer work. He was once a cook and fisherman who would leave his outport home and head to the offshore—sometimes for six months at a time. His livelihood came to an end when Jennifer was barely more than a toddler. A piece of the ship's rigging slammed into his leg, and the damage would leave him disabled for a lifetime. But his youngest daughter treasures his time at home. Especially on days like this. Today there's no pain, no swelling in that old leg, and he's ready for an evening out with his daughter.

Though only a teenager, Jennifer and her sisters have been women from a young age. Each day, she cleans and cares for their household, as their mother works to provide a modest income. And there were times the workload was even heavier. Jennifer's aging and ill grandparents also lived with them for a while. Her grandmother battling advanced diabetes, while her grandfather faced the cancer that would eventually take his life.

The only time there weren't chores was Sunday. Their family was like many in the outports on the island, when it came to matters of faith. On the Sabbath Day, there was no work. She remembers how even the vegetables for Sunday dinner had to be peeled the night before. In the morning, her mother would dress up in her Salvation Army uniform, while Jennifer and her father would stay at home to prepare dinner.

Oh what a pleasure those Sunday mornings used to be. With the vegetables boiling, Dad would pour up two cups of the broth. He'd carry them to the table along with a couple of thick slices of homemade bread. He and Jennifer would laugh and talk about the week gone by as they soaked up the broth with the bread. The dishes would wait until Monday.

But at the moment, she puts all her chores and concerns to one side. She writes as fast as her hand can travel across the page, and her homework is a necessary chore she wants to put behind her quickly.

Today Dad is feeling his usual fun self, and he's getting ready to make his way up Hicks Hill to do what they love best—visiting friends.

"I'm finished," yells Jennifer.

Her father gathers up his coat, and the two head up over the hill for a night of socializing. They know every one of the families who live in the little white houses along the lane. In fact, they are all related in some way or another. In every house, food is eagerly offered up by the hosts, and in return, Cyril Hicks offers up his brand of storytelling, of long days at sea and the adventures he once faced. In the kitchen of each home, Jennifer sits close to her dad and enjoys the sweets that are offered up. All the while, she listens ever so carefully to the cheerful and wonderful stories her dad shares. And she enjoys the appreciation shown by his audience, even though many of the stories have been heard before.

It will be midnight before these two make their way back down over the hill.

It's one of the good times, one of the positive memories Jennifer has of growing up in a community where not all the memories were so bright. Life wasn't always so easy and her family has faced many private struggles.

But through the struggles of daily life, one thing remained clear to a young Jennifer Hicks.

A father's love was the most valuable gift a daughter could ever know.

2

It had been a long school year, and a long winter, for Jennifer. Here on the edge of the ocean, the bitter northeasterly winds had kept spring out of reach for the past two months. Finally, mid-June was bringing the first of the summer like temperatures.

Today was one of the first where the students could walk to class without wearing a jacket.

Jennifer, at nearly sixteen years old, is so proud to be able to wear her new spring blouse. Of course, it's perfectly matched with the rest of her outfit. As always, her hair was styled with precision so each glossy ringlet was perfectly aligned with the next.

Jennifer quietly placed her pencil upon her desk, satisfied with the answers she had calculated. It looked as though she was the first of the class to finish the final exam in grade nine math, and that was fine with her. For the next half-hour, she could relax and feel the sun beaming through the classroom window. All the while, she dreamed of the summer ahead.

She had already established a list of families around the harbour who relied upon her for babysitting services, and she had proven her reputation as an excellent house cleaner as well. So finding work and money to pay for some summer fun would not be an issue.

Jennifer's best friend is her older sister Susan. Rarely would either of them be seen around the harbour without the other. The girls loved to hitchhike, and come the summer, that's exactly what they planned to do. They would work by day, and when they weren't making money, they would hitchhike their way to the neighbouring communities. Two attractive young women who, together, were enjoying a vibrant teenaged life.

"Okay," said the math teacher out of the silence, startling the daydreaming girl. "Turn in your papers on the way out the door, folks."

Even as she realized this school year was about to end, Jennifer knew in her heart that she wouldn't be returning to school in the fall.

3

Jennifer's hand shook from exhaustion as she squeezed the tea bag against the side of the cup. It's 6:00 a.m. and her day is about to begin despite only having four hours sleep. She's as tired as a new mother. In fact, many mothers would never know the kind of struggle she faces in caring for her three nieces—two with special needs.

Last night, she and her sister Susan had arrived home with the kids at around eleven o'clock. For the past week, they had been 400 kilometres away in St. John's at the province's only children's hospital. Susan, now twenty-one, has three children. The oldest is five. The toddlers both have cerebral palsy, and Susan is studying business administration at the local community college.

Susan is already in the shower on this morning, and Jennifer doesn't mind preparing breakfast. The rare peace and quiet of early mornings are celebrated with toast and tea. It's a chance for the sisters to have moments like those of their childhood, when their parents were still married. Today, however, their family and their parents, have moved in separate directions. All except Jennifer and Susan.

Jennifer hears the water shut off in the washroom as she sips her tea. When the sisters moved to Gander, they were both accepted in the business administration program at the local college. But Jennifer was happier doing what she loved best. And what she loved was the feeling of caring for those in need. Especially her sister and her beautiful nieces.

Susan came out of the washroom, dressed and ready to face the day. She sat at the table, and they ate quietly in the blue light of the morning. It was twenty below outside on this day in January, and neither woman had slept enough to recover from the past week or last night's drive.

"Jennifer, the girls have a follow-up appointment with Dr. McDonald today," said Susan. "Would you mind?"

"Of course not," said Jennifer.

"I'll get the girls' stroller ready for you. Are you sure you can handle Olivia as well?" Susan asked. "If there was a way I could take today off class, you know I would. I've just missed the past week because of the hospital stay, and I don't know how many more missed days my instructor will tolerate."

"It's not a problem, Susan, you don't have a thing to worry about," said Jennifer.

Holding back the tears, Susan accepted her sister's help. But quietly she worries about Jennifer. While Jennifer didn't talk about having a family of her own, Susan knows, deep down, her sister wants her own children to care for and nurture.

"As soon as we get this worked out, you have to make sure you're enrolled back into the program this September. This isn't fair to you, Jennifer."

But as usual, Jennifer put her own needs aside once again. This time it was to help Susan, and especially her nieces. She was at her best when she was taking care of others.

Especially those who needed the extra attention.

A young Jennifer Hicks spent most of her teenaged years babysitting around her community. Here she is with her two nieces and nephew, whom she cared for in the first months after she had left her hometown to live in Gander.

4

Susan didn't have to worry about Jennifer for long. Within a few weeks, Susan decided that her family and the needs of her children were more important than school at this point in her life. She quit college, and Jennifer suddenly found herself with a lot more time on her hands.

"I think it's time I start making some money again,"

said Jennifer one evening early in the spring. The kids were in bed. She was watching television with her sister, when she made the decision that the next day she would begin searching for work. The next morning she was up at the break of dawn. She had a long, hot shower and then spent time putting together the perfect outfit. She styled her hair and applied her makeup with precision.

Jennifer believed that, without a high school diploma, her ability to clean and organize would be her best skills for employability. She'd also worked at a Chinese restaurant in her hometown, so she had some skills to offer up. She bundled up in her warmest jacket, gathered up her resumes, and made her way to the strip of hotels along the Trans-Canada Highway. Jennifer knew finding work wouldn't be an easy task. Even minimum-wage jobs were hard to come by in Newfoundland these days.

The first hotel was just minutes from her apartment, and working here would be ideal. But that wasn't to be. They took her resume, but she got the standard line. "We have nothing to offer at this time." However, a short distance down the road, she caught a lucky break. Just two days ago, an employee at the Albatross had to leave on short notice. The hotel was playing host to several conferences, and management was desperate for a waitress.

"When can you start?" asked the manager.

"Right away," said Jennifer. And within minutes she was learning the ropes. She studied the menu and learned her new responsibilities. That night she went home knowing that she had earned a good day's pay, not to mention $33 in tips.

In a few days, Jennifer was quite comfortable waiting tables in the hotel dining room. She was quick on her feet and had no trouble getting the orders right.

As days passed, she grew more efficient at her job. And she was also glad to be having a bit of a social life. In early

May, she met a fellow one night at the bar, and they began dating.

For Jennifer, things were starting to fall in place.

"Jennifer—phone!" yelled Susan from the bedroom. "It's Cara."

Cara was one of Jennifer's co-workers at the restaurant, and the two had quickly become good friends. A Saturday mid-afternoon phone call probably meant she was hoping she and Jennifer would be getting together for a night on the town. But that wasn't the case at all.

"Hey, girl, we need to talk," she said. "It's important news about that sleaze you're dating."

"Really? What's the matter?" asked Jennifer.

"Are you sure you want to hear this over the phone?" asked Cara. "That guy has been sleeping around. You know the girl who was with us at the bar last week? Well, he's been seeing her behind your back. She's pregnant, Jennifer."

Jennifer hung up. She hadn't been in love with the guy, but she was hurt nonetheless. And she was mad.

She picked up the phone once more and dialled his number.

"You know what?" she growled into the phone. "I'm not asking you to choose between me and her. I'm making the choice for you."

And those were the last words she had spoken to him.

It took some time to come to terms with what had happened, but certainly everything was not all bad in her romantic life. Jennifer's pride in her appearance made her a bit of a catch around the neighbourhood. One soldier in particular would have stopped at nothing for a date. Kevin had been stationed at Canadian Forces Base Gander for two years now, and Jennifer was just his type. Every Friday, he'd call her up hoping this would be the weekend she'd say yes to a date. But for several reasons Jennifer just wasn't interested.

"I can't imagine getting involved with someone in the

military and having to move around all the time," Jennifer said one day as she and Susan were visiting their friends John and Nicole one afternoon.

"Gander is big enough for me," she said. "What would I do living in the big cities on the mainland?"

"I don't know," said Nicole. "That man is determined, and I think you could have a pretty good life with him."

"Well, I don't have any interest in moving around on the mainland," snapped Jennifer.

The two sisters finished up their laughs and gossip with their neighbours and headed home for the afternoon.

They walked down the steps and headed across the walkway to their own building.

Along the way, Susan pointed out a fellow standing at the end of the walkway. "I wonder who that guy is," she said. "He sure seems to be around quite a bit lately. He must be living in the building."

Jennifer shrugged and continued the short walk back to her apartment building.

The buildings in Gander where both Jennifer and Nelson lived when they first met back in 1997. Photo by Colleen Lewis.

5

Gander was finally beginning to feel more and more like home for the Hicks sisters. Jennifer was enjoying her work and had a busy social life as well. And on those rare days they found themselves with nothing to do, the girls loved having coffee with their neighbours.

Last night, they had been out dancing until the early morning hours, and now Jennifer was preparing for yet another busy day. She and Susan had doctor appointments for the girls at noon, they needed groceries, and Jennifer was working the evening shift for a large wedding at the hotel.

Getting the girls ready was no easy task, even with two adults sharing the work. With the girls' limited mobility, it was sometimes tough getting them from the bath to the stroller.

Then there were the stairs to contend with. Living on the third floor with no elevator made mundane tasks seem impossible.

Today was no exception, but it was a job Jennifer cherished. She felt so happy to be able to take care of the nieces she loved so much.

Susan was getting the girls' shoes on, while Jennifer was finishing up the last of the morning dishes.

Finally, everything was in order and they were headed downstairs with the two smallest children in their strollers and the oldest walking alongside. As they crossed the parking lot, Jennifer noticed the odd man again. He appeared to be just quietly watching, but she made nothing of it. There were plenty of strange folks hanging around here in the heat of the summer.

They continued up the street and toward the medical clinic when Susan made a realization.

"Oh my God, Jennifer, how could I be so stupid? I've forgotten everything," she said. "I need their medications and some information the specialist in St. John's gave me. There's a big yellow envelope sitting on the table, along with a paper bag with their pills."

"Don't worry," said Jennifer. "I'll catch up in a minute."

Jennifer broke into a near-jog to make sure her sister had everything she needed for the appointment, and there wasn't much time.

She burst through the front door and up the steps. In a moment she was bouncing back down the stairwell with the items in her hand. She sprinted back outside, only to come to a complete and sudden stop that nearly took her breath away.

Standing in her path was the man she and her sister had noticed hanging about. He wasn't tall, and he had dark hair and dark eyes. His shoulders were broad and there was nowhere for Jennifer to run. When she tried to run to the left, he swiftly shifted his large body to block her path. And then he smiled.

She tried to go around him to the right. Again he blocked her. This time he laughed.

Frustrated, and a little scared, Jennifer pushed through to her left once more and finally made it past the intimidating man. Glancing over her shoulder, she realized he was laughing.

What was that? she thought. *What a weird fellow.*

Farther up the road, she turned around to look.

He was still watching, and grinning, like a child who had gotten the attention he was after.

"Nelson Hart," said Nicole. "Dean is actually helping him move today. He's moving upstairs from building number three. They've been at it for the past couple of hours.

"To be honest, Jennifer, I'm not sure what his story is.

I believe there are some sort of health issues with him," explained Nicole. "I know he does have a home care worker over there. I think he gets a lot of help from his mother as well. He pops over from time to time for a chat."

"Well, he's awfully strange," said Jennifer. "He's blocked my path at least half a dozen times now. He doesn't say anything, just stands there and laughs. What's even stranger is that he doesn't do anything when there's someone with me.

"Susan and I have passed by him a number of times now. He doesn't speak or anything. Just watches us," said Jennifer. "But when I'm alone, he blocks my way and laughs. To be honest, I'm a little scared of him."

"Oh, don't worry," said Nicole. "He's a little strange, but once you get to know him, he's no different than the rest of us, I suppose."

Nicole was pouring up another cup of coffee when her boyfriend burst through the door.

"He's dying," screamed Dean, who could barely catch his breath.

"What the hell are you talking about?" shrieked Nicole. She could see the panic in his eyes.

"It's Nelson," he gasped. "Upstairs. He's dying on the floor."

With that, Jennifer and Nicole ran up the stairs and into Nelson's apartment. He was on the floor, his entire body shaking intensely, and his mouth was foaming.

"Out of the way," said Jennifer as she made her way over to him.

This wasn't the first time Jennifer had seen this type of seizure. She had seen it many times with her own sister. She quickly put a pillow under his head and called the ambulance.

After a few minutes, he came around, but was slightly confused. She could see he was also exhausted from the seizure. They helped him up onto the couch. Jennifer looked around at the stunned faces of her neighbours, and she was glad she was there to help.

6

The next time she saw Nelson Hart, they were both at Nicole's apartment, and there was no mention of either his seizure or their awkward encounters in the parking lot.

But the more they chatted, the more she saw him as a decent guy. He spoke confidently, but he was also humble. Even a bit shy, she observed.

Slowly she began to relax in his company as they continued to drink coffee and share the local gossip. Finally, it was time to go home.

"He seemed kind of normal," laughed Susan as they made their way down the path. "After the stories you told me about him, I was expecting a monster. To be honest, Jennifer, he was looking at you like he was interested in more than just playing tag in the parking lot."

"Well, he's not as odd as I first thought, but I'm still not sure I'd want to go out with him," said Jennifer.

But Nelson Hart was starting to grow on Jennifer. She couldn't put her finger on it, but there was something oddly attractive about him.

The next time Jennifer dropped by for a visit with her neighbours, an eager Nelson showed up within minutes. With no job, there was plenty of time for Nelson to kill during a day.

This time he sat next to Jennifer.

"Are you working today?" he asked her.

"No, it's my day off. I just finished eight days straight," she said. "I need to ask you something, Nelson. Why have you been blocking my path every time we see each other in the parking lot? I don't understand."

Nelson lowered his head and suddenly took on a very boyish demeanour.

"That's the only way I knew how to let you know I liked you," he mumbled.

After a considerable silence, he spoke once more. This time it was to ask her if she wanted to go out on a date.

Jennifer wasn't sure what to think. Should she go out with this guy? He was odd. But he was nice. And there was something about him that made her feel like he could take care of her, protect her.

"Sure," she said.

They agreed that he would come by her apartment at seven. Shortly after their conversation, he left Nicole's apartment, and Jennifer went to her building to get ready.

She wondered what he had in mind for a date as she got ready.

She started with a long shower. Thoroughly washing her hair. As always, getting ready for Jennifer would take some time. But by six thirty she was ready and impeccably groomed.

Of course, neither Jennifer nor Nelson owned a car, so they were limited in their options as to how they would spend the evening. But they really weren't concerned with what they would do.

They left the apartment and just started to walk.

They walked through downtown, talking about their backgrounds. Nelson explained how he had grown up on the northeast coast as well. He was raised in the small town of Horwood and had moved to Gander.

He told her more about his seizures.

Some were minor, but the grand mal seizures could leave him feeling exhausted for days. The seizures were serious enough that he had lost his driver's licence.

After an hour or so, he took Jennifer's hand, and they instantly became a pair. It certainly wasn't a typical date.

There were no flowers and he didn't buy her dinner. They strolled from store to store, eyeing luxuries that neither of them could afford. And at the moment, neither of them cared for anything but each other's company.

That night they went back to their respective apartments, knowing there would be a second date.

It was a couple of days before Jennifer could get an evening off work. But she was excited about the prospects of another evening with Nelson.

"You're seeing him again tonight?" Susan asked.

When date night finally arrived, Jennifer was really looking forward to being with him again. There was something in his personality that continued to draw her toward him, though she could still not quite pinpoint what it was.

"Yup. I'm really excited about seeing him again, too. He's just a good fellow," said Jennifer.

Finally, Nelson knocked on the door, and he and Jennifer headed out for the evening.

"See you later," Jennifer said to her sister.

From that day forward, the two were rarely seen apart.

7

It was October.

Jennifer followed Nelson up the long flight of stairs to his apartment. It was her first time visiting his place, but in her heart she already knew that at some point she would probably be calling this apartment home.

Depending on how things went today, of course.

Jennifer was anxious to see how he lived. She had firm values when it came to cleanliness. Not just over her personal hygiene, but she also believed a person's living environment should be equally pristine.

"Come on in," said Nelson.

Jennifer slowly proceeded through the doorway, fearing the worst. Instead, she found an apartment that was absolutely spotless. Nothing was out of place, the floors were clean, the countertops were tidy, and the furniture was modest but in good condition.

"I'm impressed," said Jennifer. "You like to keep things clean."

"Well," he said. "It's not entirely my doing. I have a personal care worker who comes by a few times a week. Government pays me $300 a month to hire her, because of the seizures. When she doesn't come, Mom usually helps out.

"You should move in here," suggested Nelson.

It wasn't a request she had expected to hear so soon. Jennifer was taken aback, but at the same time, the idea excited her. Living with Nelson would mean she could finally have a place to call her own. Also, Nelson had become her best friend. It would be nice to have him near her each night. And as much as she loved her sister, the apartment was getting more and more crowded as her nieces grew older.

Plus, there was part of her that felt like Nelson could use her help, no matter how self-sufficient he appeared to be.

"All right, it's a done deal," she blurted out.

Within two days they had packed all her belongings and moved them across the street to building number three.

To her new home and partner.

8

Jennifer rolls over and looks at the numbers on the alarm clock. Finally, a place to call her own.

Jennifer had never felt better in her life than at this moment. Her job was perfect, and the tips were great. Nelson had welcomed her into his home, and it felt like her place.

It was somewhat challenging as she rounded up her belongings and figured out what space would be hers. But that morning she felt comfortable there. Lying in his bed, she watched him sleep. She hoped this was the man she would spend the rest of her life with. Even though he seemed to need a lot of help, there was something about Nelson that made Jennifer feel safe and wanted.

As a couple, they didn't go to fancy places or even to the bar much. But it was a good relationship.

This would be a great Christmas, she was sure.

"Nelson," shouted a voice from the living room. "Are you up?"

Jennifer was startled. Who would be in his apartment while they were still in bed?"

"That's Mom," said Nelson. "What the hell does she think she's at?"

Jennifer scrambled to get dressed. Nelson was already in his clothes and out in the living room. She couldn't hear what they were saying, but she could tell by the sound of their voices that they weren't getting along. Nelson hadn't really talked a lot about his mother, but Jennifer already knew their relationship was strained.

"Hello," said Jennifer as she made her way into the room.

"Hi. I see you have all your things moved in. Is everything okay?"

"Yeah. We had a bit of a late night, though."

9

It was March. Not the best time of year for travelling on the Trans-Canada Highway in Newfoundland, but Nelson and Jennifer decided to help out a friend.

Stacy needed to take a four-hour trip into St. John's to visit her son in the hospital, and she was going to take a taxi. But she didn't want to go alone, so Jennifer and Nelson decided to tag along for company. They were up and ready to go before sunrise.

"Are you sure you can drive around the city?" Jennifer asked the cabbie as they got into the car.

But they were barely in St. John's before they realized the taxi driver wasn't exactly used to city driving, and they encountered several problems trying to get to the hospital. In fact, it took two hours of driving around the city before they finally reached their destination.

Amazingly, they managed to get there on time. But after managing the traffic, they were then tasked with navigating their way around a massive hospital to find Stacy's son.

For part of the day they gave Stacy some privacy, but they also spent some time visiting as well.

Jennifer was glad, though, when they finally left St. John's that evening. The weather had taken a turn for the worse and a spring storm was moving in.

"Are you sure we should drive back in this weather?" Jennifer asked the driver. He didn't say anything, and the three of them piled into the car anyway. Out on the highway, Jennifer was getting nervous.

"Slow down," she yelled. She was watching the speedometer and could hardly believe the driver was reaching speeds of 110 kph in the snow and slush. "You're going to get us all killed."

"Listen here," he said. "I've got to have this car back in Gander in a couple of hours, so there's no time to spare."

It was 2:00 p.m. and they were just approaching Clarenville. Jennifer knew there was no way the driver would make it back in time, and she was afraid for her life.

From time to time she could feel the car swaying when he'd pull out to pass. Several times she caught herself gritting her teeth in fear.

She had taken her eyes away from the window for only a moment when she looked up to see the trees flying past the car and scraping the windows. They hit several hard bumps before the car eventually came to a halt in the ditch.

The driver opened his door and got out, as did her friend Stacy, who was in the back seat with Jennifer.

At first Jennifer was afraid to move, unsure of whether or not she was injured. But she quickly came to her senses.

Nelson was crying. Shrieking, more like it, in the front seat. His head was slumped down between the two seats in an unnatural position. Jennifer quickly and gently grabbed his head and repositioned it up against the back of the seat. The cab driver waved down help, and it wasn't long before all four of them were on their way to the hospital in Clarenville. The paramedics had placed a collar on Nelson's neck, but he continued to scream in pain.

At the hospital, everyone was examined and released, even Nelson. Of course, Jennifer stayed by his side through a variety of tests. Finally, the doctor simply explained that he would need follow-up treatment at the hospital in Gander.

Jennifer and Nelson made it back to their apartment late that evening. Jennifer went to bed, but Nelson decided to sleep on the couch. As Jennifer was getting dressed, she decided to check in on Nelson once more before getting some much-needed sleep.

To her surprise, he was trying to reach the phone.

"Who are you calling at this hour?" she asked.

"I have to go the hospital now," he replied. "Something's not right."

At four o'clock in the morning, Jennifer and Nelson were on their way back to St. John's, this time on board an air ambulance.

Doctors and nurses were rushing around and explaining things that Jennifer didn't understand. In the end she learned that Nelson had broken his C2 vertebrae and was lucky to be alive. But there was a long road of recovery ahead.

For the next twenty-six days, Jennifer slept sitting in a

chair by Nelson's bedside in the hospital. She returned to the hostel only to shower and change, but Nelson always hated for her to leave.

When he was finally able to return home, there was only temporary relief for Jennifer. Infection set into his wounds.

They ended up back in the hospital, where, again, Jennifer would spend weeks sitting by Nelson's bedside as he recovered.

10

With the winter, and Nelson's injuries, behind them, that June was especially welcomed. Life was finally returning to normal.

Nelson had been up late the night before, and this morning he was still asleep. Jennifer expected he wouldn't be getting up for at least a couple of hours.

She kept the volume of the radio on low, trying not to wake him. Nelson hated to wake up before he was ready. She started getting ready for the day ahead as quietly as she could. Even though breakfast wasn't started, she was contemplating what to take out of the freezer for tonight's supper.

But surprisingly, her thoughts were abruptly interrupted when she heard Nelson slowly waking up and shuffling around the room. She stuck her head out around the corner to have a look in the bedroom, and sure enough, he was sitting on the edge of the bed.

"You should go back to sleep," she said. "You had a late night." The truth was Nelson slept a lot, but she found it a lot easier to get her chores done when he was out of the way.

No answer.

Jennifer switched her tasks and started in on making Nelson's breakfast. Toast, eggs, fried potato, and bologna.

Jennifer quickly got to work. She dragged out the old frying pan and started heating the oil.

But Nelson's silence was somewhat unusual, and she had another look around the corner. He was in the washroom.

She went back to running the water for the kettle when she heard his voice coming from the bathroom. He was obviously talking to himself, but she couldn't understand what he was saying. The one thing she could gather was that he certainly wasn't in a good mood. He sounded like he was complaining. Almost mad.

"What's the matter?" she sang out.

"Nothing. Shut up," he said.

Suddenly, without warning, Nelson stormed into the room with a look she hadn't seen on anyone before.

He wasn't just grumpy. He was enraged and hysterical at the same time.

"What the hell is wrong?" Jennifer shrieked.

He hissed, and one large fist lifted into the air above his head and came crashing down onto the coffee table. It smashed into two pieces.

He grabbed one piece and threw it at the wall. Another one flew into the apartment door.

Jennifer was suddenly afraid of the flying debris as Nelson continued to curse and single-handedly destroyed the coffee table in a matter of minutes.

He finally stopped.

He stood there, breathing intensely. But the look did not leave his eyes.

Jennifer came out from behind the shelter of the kitchen wall and went straight to the phone.

She shook as she pushed the numbers that would reach her mother.

"Mom, you have to come get me," she stammered. "Something's wrong with Nelson."

"We'll be there in a couple of hours," her mother said.

"My son, there's something wrong with you," Jennifer yelled. Then she went straight to her room and shut the door, where she stayed until her parents got there. It would take a while before they arrived. They had to make the long drive from the south coast of Newfoundland, but they didn't hesitate. They had sensed the urgency in Jennifer's voice.

She felt mesmerized as she packed her bag with the bedroom door locked behind her. Was this fit because of the accident? What kind of explanation could there be? There was no warning. No clues. She didn't believe she had done anything wrong. Even in the midst of the tantrum, he gave no clue or reason as to why he was upset.

There's something seriously wrong here, she thought. But at the same time, she also felt a deep pity for Nelson and a need to help him through whatever was happening to him.

Finally, she heard her mother's voice outside. "Where is Jennifer?"

"In the room," said Nelson.

Jennifer could hear him stomping down the stairwell while her mother was knocking on her bedroom door.

Within minutes Jennifer was in her mother's car and on her way to St. Alban's.

So much had happened. How could things go from so good to so bad in such a short period? What was the trigger? Had something happened between him and his mother? Was he choosing not to tell her whatever it was? Either way, Jennifer wasn't taking a chance on having to see him like that again. If he had hit her like that, she'd have ended up in the hospital.

Whatever was going on with Nelson, she put it behind her for the moment. Jennifer was happy to spend some time with her family. She loved the evenings by the wood stove with her mother and stepfather. Pat had been like a father to Jennifer and her sisters, and that's how the girls viewed him.

She felt safe here in St. Alban's, and she was in no hurry to leave.

However, it was only a few days before the phone rang. It was Nelson, looking for Jennifer.

"I'm sorry, I don't know what happened," he said.

"I don't feel like it's a safe environment for me to be in, Nelson," said Jennifer.

The next call was also from Gander.

"You need to come back. Nelson is having a hard time without you. You know he was only in a bad mood, right? Sure, he wouldn't have hurt you. Come back and it will all work out."

"I don't like him," said Pat. "I don't know what it is, Jennifer, but something just isn't right."

But Nelson wasn't about to give up. The phone calls continued. Each time, more and more was promised. Each time, he begged for forgiveness.

"Maybe it was just this once," Jennifer told her family. "Perhaps it will be different. I really feel like I need to try. Maybe it's just his sickness, and I'm the only one who can truly help him."

"I don't think it's that's simple," Pat told her. "But you do whatever you feel you need to do."

The next morning, Jennifer was nervous about her decision as she sat in the back seat of Pat's car in front of the apartment building. Pat was getting her bags out of the trunk. Though she didn't like Nelson's dark side, she was also looking forward to seeing him again.

"Thanks for the help, and for letting me stay at your place." Jennifer hugged her mother and Pat. "I know you guys don't have much room, and I appreciate you letting me stay there."

After their goodbyes, Jennifer walked up the steps to the apartment and let herself in.

The coffee table had been replaced with a newer one. Shining wood. Like nothing had happened.

11

Dry toast was on the menu for Jennifer's breakfast. She had only been back from St. Alban's for a few days, but she hadn't been feeling well.

"You're not having much to eat," mumbled Nelson as he made his way to the couch to watch television.

"I already told you! I'm sick," said Jennifer. "And why do you have to spend all your time sitting on that bloody couch? You're either sleeping or watching TV day and night."

No response.

One bite was about all Jennifer's stomach could handle this morning. She figured something was definitely wrong, and it was about time she saw a doctor.

"Nelson, I need to walk to the doctor's office. Can you come with me?" she asked.

No response.

Between episodes of vomiting, Jennifer managed to get dressed and make her way down Bennett Avenue to see her family doctor, alone.

"The first thing we need to do is to arrange for some blood work and a urine sample," said Dr. McDonald. "Is there any chance you could be pregnant?"

Jennifer was speechless. With everything that had happened in her life since meeting Nelson, she hadn't had a chance to even consider having children.

"I . . . I . . . I guess there's a chance," she managed to say.

"Well, sounds to me like you may be having morning sickness," said Dr. McDonald. "But let's find out for sure."

Jennifer left his office and made the ten-minute walk to the hospital. With her empty stomach, there was no problem getting lab work done this morning.

But on her walk home, she had time to think. With each

step, reality began to sink in. *I am pregnant*, she thought. *It makes sense now*.

But what about Nelson? Was he capable of being a father? There was so much work in looking after him, she thought. Maybe he would change. Maybe having a child to look after would get him off the couch.

She quickly put Nelson out of her mind and thought about what life would be like with a child.

Fear turned to excitement.

As she walked home that afternoon, she didn't need a doctor to tell her she was pregnant.

She already knew.

When she got home, Nelson was in his usual spot, perched in front of the television, oblivious to the world around him. Jennifer had no intention of sharing her thoughts with him. And that certainly wasn't difficult, considering Nelson hadn't even asked how her doctor appointment had gone.

For the next two days, she went about her business as normal. Until the time came to go back to the doctor for her results.

"Well," said Dr. McDonald. "There's no question about it, you're definitely pregnant."

Jennifer had already had time to absorb the changes that were about to occur in her life. But hearing those words still had a quite an impact.

Her senses were heightened. She was elated at the thought of having her own little family, and she couldn't stop smiling as the doctor passed her a handful of brochures. There were instructions about her nutrition, vitamins she would have to take, appointments that would have to be made.

It was all a dream come true. She could barely stop herself from running down the street as she went home to tell Nelson.

She walked into the apartment and set about making supper right away. The moment had to be right when she told him, and making his favourite meal would be a start to setting the mood.

He didn't say much, just kept watching the television and flicking through the channels.

The two of them sat down and ate without saying much at all. Jennifer was waiting for just the right moment, when suddenly she just blurted it out.

"Guess what," she said. "We're soon going to need a bigger apartment. I'm pregnant."

Nelson poked his fork around in the mashed potato. He didn't say a word.

Jennifer had never felt so uncomfortable in her life. The seconds felt like minutes. She felt feverish. It was almost as if she was about to faint. He wasn't excited in the least. In fact, she believed he was far from happy.

After what seemed like an eternity of silence, she asked him, "Aren't you going to say anything, my son?"

"I guess it's all right," he said.

It wasn't exactly the response Jennifer was hoping for. And as much as she was excited about having a child, there was one thought that suddenly crossed her mind. It filled her with dread.

If he was like this now, what was he going to be like as a father?

12

With the morning sickness out of the way, Jennifer couldn't ever remember feeling better. Nelson spent most of his time sleeping, and that gave her time to decorate the apartment and accomplish all her goals in the remaining months before the new baby came along.

Things were also looking up with Nelson. He had finally

begun to show some emotion about becoming a new father. Last week they were out shopping, and at times he even seemed to enjoy looking through the baby clothes. Though with only their welfare cheque to rely on, there wasn't much money to go around for anything related to the new baby.

Luckily, there was still plenty of time left in the pregnancy for Jennifer to help Nelson warm up to the idea of having a child.

But it wouldn't be as easy as she'd hoped.

"Nelson," yelled Jennifer over the sound of the television. "Tomorrow is my ultrasound. That means we can actually see our baby. The appointment is at two o'clock. Don't forget."

She shook her head as she walked away. Sometimes she wondered if he was even listening at all.

The next morning, Jennifer went through her preparations, which included drinking plenty of water. By one o'clock she was badly in need of a pee. But that would have to wait.

"I'm not going," said Nelson.

"What did you just say?"

"I don't want to go, I'm tired," he said.

Jennifer sighed. She wasn't totally surprised, and now she had bigger things to worry about. Nelson just wasn't as excited as she'd hoped, but now she also had to make it to the hospital with an extremely full bladder. She got dressed and walked to the medical clinic, alone. There were many times her stomach hurt so badly she never thought she'd make it.

"Jennifer Hicks, room three," rang out over the hospital PA system.

Jennifer could barely walk, she needed to pee so badly. But that was nothing compared to her excitement over finally getting to see her child.

She climbed up onto the hard table and lifted her shirt

as she was instructed to do. The warm gel was placed on her stomach, and she lay there as the technician did her job.

For what seemed like an eternity, the ultrasound technician moved the transducer around her growing belly. She carefully watched her expression studying the baby ever so carefully. Every few seconds there was a click, and Jennifer was growing more anxious by the minute. It seemed as though there was something bothering the ultrasound technician, and Jennifer couldn't help but worry something was wrong.

"I have some news for you," the woman said.

Jennifer couldn't even speak, she was so scared. At that moment she wished someone were here to help her through this.

"Look at the screen," she said.

Jennifer lifted herself up onto her side to look at the blurry dark image.

"This is your baby's head," she said. "But as you can see, here is the second head. Congratulations, Jennifer, it looks like you're having twins."

It was something that Jennifer had always wished for. Two babies, born at the same time! They would grow together and have each other for a lifetime. Her only hope was that they would be of the same sex. She was already dreaming about putting them in matching outfits, and the fun they would have.

13

As she expected, Nelson handled the news the same way he treated the pregnancy. There was no reaction of surprise, shock, or joy. He just went on changing channels and sleeping the days away.

But for Jennifer there were things to be done. The money wasn't there for decorating, but she had plenty to keep her busy.

Besides her regular medical checkups, she also had to start prenatal classes.

"The classes are extremely important," she explained to Nelson. "This will teach me how to deal with the labour, and what to expect." She begged him to go with her, but Nelson refused to attend.

But that wasn't stopping her from making sure her babies would be well taken care of right from their very first moments.

On the first class that Wednesday evening, she bundled up and walked across town by herself to be part of the prenatal class.

She was the only single mother in the room, but she learned about the importance of her nutrition and about some of the exercises she should be doing to stay healthy.

For the most part, the things she learned were things she had already adapted into her lifestyle since she had found out she was pregnant. Her doctor agreed that she had never been healthier, and he was happy to see her being so careful about her condition.

There were ten other people taking the class with her. She was the only expectant mom to be there alone, and at first she didn't care. But it became more difficult as the couples joked about the cravings and other things that came with pregnancy.

And it didn't get easier. When they moved on to topics discussing how important it was for the dad to support the mother during pregnancy, Jennifer longed for Nelson's support. As she watched the husbands learn how to comfort their wives in labour, Jennifer had never felt so alone.

Her second prenatal class would be her last.

"What is wrong with you, my son?" she snapped after she came home from the class. Jennifer was yelling even before she had time to shut the apartment door. "All the other fathers go to the meetings. Why can't you? Why?"

she screamed at him. "I want to make sure I have healthy babies, and all you want to do is lie around this apartment and watch that damn television."

She raged on for several minutes, but Nelson still had nothing to say.

14

Friday morning.

Jennifer was half asleep when she felt Nelson nudging her.

"What time is it?" she asked.

"It's nine o'clock," said Nelson. "You need to go have your blood work done today. Lets go."

"That's not until this afternoon, Nelson. I need to get up, shower, and get breakfast." Jennifer was confused. It wasn't like Nelson to take an interest in anything she had to do, and here he was waking her for an appointment that was still hours away.

"I want to leave now," he said.

Jennifer sat up. She could see the panic in his face, and she knew something wasn't right.

"Nelson, we don't have to leave for a few hours. You're going to have to wait."

What happened next was beyond anything she could have anticipated.

Nelson began to yell and started slamming his forehead into the bedroom wall. It wasn't a seizure, that much Jennifer knew for sure. But he was hitting his head hard enough that she expected to see him put a hole clear through the drywall. Suddenly, he grabbed his hair and pulled out a handful. He continued to smash his head into the wall. There had been too many strikes now for Jennifer to count.

Suddenly, he began to wail again and dropped to the floor on his knees. He continued to hit his head against the floor.

Jennifer didn't know where to turn. She ran to the phone and dialled Nelson's mother.

"There's something wrong with Nelson. He's hitting his head against the wall and the floor. I'm afraid he's going to really hurt himself."

Within minutes, Nelson's mother was there. She talked him down out of his rage and stayed with him until Jennifer returned home from her appointment.

By then, everything appeared to have returned to normal. It seemed to Jennifer that this wasn't the first time his mother had dealt with "one of his fits."

15

Despite being extra careful about everything she ate, getting around was becoming more and more difficult for Jennifer in the months leading up to the winter of 1999.

Being pregnant with twins meant the doctors wanted to keep a close eye on the pregnancy. Of course, that meant regular visits to the doctor's office.

Jennifer walked over to the apartment's main window and looked out at the falling snow. It had been snowing for most of the morning, and the roads were a mixture of watery puddles and slush.

"Nelson, I have to go to the clinic this afternoon. Is there enough money for a taxi? I really don't feel like walking."

"Huh," he laughed. "You don't need a cab to walk over to the clinic."

That was the last he had to say on the matter. He got up off the couch and started to get dressed.

Jennifer didn't need to ask where he was going. Nelson and his mother had started spending time at the bar together. He wasn't a drinker, but Jennifer knew he and his mother liked to play the slots together.

Oh well, at least I won't have to deal with him this afternoon, she thought.

But the walk to the clinic proved to be just as difficult as she expected. Her feet quickly got wet, and she was finding herself getting tired quickly. Then she had to contend with the icy sidewalks, which she hadn't expected today.

She was relieved to finally sit in the clinic waiting room, and she was also glad there would be a long wait to see the doctor today. At least here she could relax.

After about forty minutes, Dr. McDonald's receptionist finally called her into his office.

"Jennifer, you look exhausted. Are you taking care of yourself? Eating right? Getting enough sleep?" he asked.

"I'm following all your orders. It's just that I had to walk here today, and it's kind of worn me out."

Dr. McDonald looked at her, puzzled. "Where is your boyfriend? Did you walk here alone in this weather?"

"Yes," she replied.

"I know it isn't easy for you, but you are going to need help," he said. "Is there someone who can drive you?"

His words echoed in Jennifer's mind as she walked home.

By the time she got home, her feet were freezing and strands of her hair had clumped together around her face.

That's enough of this walking around to appointments, she thought.

The next morning, Nelson agreed to help her look for a car, and she enrolled in a student driver program.

With so much work to do, and so little help from Nelson, she had the motivation she needed to get her licence.

It wasn't long before she was enrolled in driving school. While her pregnant state made the driving instructor nervous at times, she continued on. Finally, she got her driver's licence, while she was five months pregnant. By that time Nelson had found a car for her to buy. She paid

$300 for a little Chevy. The car might not have been much, but it gave her the freedom to get things done.

Suddenly, the medical appointments weren't such a large burden, and taking care of Nelson got a lot easier, too.

16

But the $300 car wasn't such a great buy. It seemed like it broke down more than it worked these days, and social services didn't provide enough money to fix cars.

"I don't understand why you don't have any money, Nelson," said Jennifer. "We only got paid last week. Did you spend the money when you were out with your mother this weekend?"

"No I didn't. Plus, it's none of your business what I do with the money, anyway," he said. "Just you wait till I get the settlement from my accident. I won't have to worry about money then."

Since the accident, Nelson was working with lawyers on a claim that he had filed against the taxi firm. Based on their legal opinions, Nelson could expect thousands of dollars in compensation. They were holding the taxi firm responsible for Nelson's injuries, but it wasn't clear when, or even if, he would get any money.

For now, the couple had to walk to the grocery store, despite Jennifer's condition. With only three weeks to go, her feet were nearly always swollen. The weight of her big belly was also taking its toll on her lower back.

But chores still needed to be done, and she was grateful that at least this time Nelson had agreed to help.

Nelson grabbed a few of the grocery bags while Jennifer carried the remaining two. She was grateful for the shortcut they had discovered. At least they would be home in five minutes or so.

As she walked out of the main entrance, Jennifer's

grocery bags dropped to the ground and her body fell forward with pain.

"Oh my God, Nelson, I think I'm in labour."

Instead of calling an ambulance, Nelson picked up her groceries, and the two began the walk down the trail.

Every couple of feet, Jennifer would double over in pain. Several times the world around her would darken and blur. Sounds would drift in and out. At times her body felt like it was on fire.

"I don't think I can make it," she moaned. But each time, Jennifer picked herself back up. She was determined to make it home.

When the apartment building came into view, she regained her strength enough to make it inside. The stairs brought their own challenge, but she continued on until she made it to her couch, where she fell down, exhausted. Right now she didn't even have the energy to call the hospital. Instead, she had a short nap. But no sooner had she dozed off than the pain woke her with a start. She got up and found the strength to call a taxi. She knew she needed to get to the hospital.

She grabbed a bag and headed back down the stairs and into the parking lot. The driver looked at her nervously as she climbed into the car, and he wasted no time getting to the hospital.

"That's it. The time has come for you to rest," said the obstetrician. "Get this girl admitted," he said to the nurse who was standing next to him.

"Right away, Dr. Kent."

He said, "Jennifer, the babies have dropped, so we have to keep a close eye on you until the surgery."

Dr. Kent was taking over from Dr. McDonald from this point on. The babies would be delivered by Caesarean section on March 15.

Jennifer had never felt so tired. She answered the

questions as the nurse checked her vitals and went through a long list of questions. They brought her a hospital gown, which would have to do until someone brought in her suitcase.

As she climbed onto the little bed, she wondered how long she would have to wait before the twins came.

For the next week, Jennifer tried her best to sleep and to enjoy her time away from chores and work. But rest didn't come easy. At night she could hear the staff in the hallways. It seemed like every time she dozed off someone would laugh or call out, waking her suddenly. By day five she was longing for a night's rest in her own bed. She was also wondering how Nelson was doing. He wasn't exactly used to being on his own, and it seemed like he was calling her every ten minutes.

"No way, Jennifer. It's too risky to let you go home at this stage," said Dr. Kent.

"But I'm only five minutes away from home," she pleaded.

Dr. Kent agreed to give it some thought.

Later the same day, Jennifer got the green light to go home, with strict orders to return if anything seemed out of the ordinary.

Dr. Kent also gave her his home phone number, in case there was an emergency.

Her first night home was the best night's sleep she'd had for a week. The next day she felt brand new.

"Do you feel well enough to run out to the store with me?" Aunt June asked. Her aunt had dropped by to see how Jennifer was holding up.

Jennifer couldn't resist the opportunity to look at the baby section. At the department store, she combed through the racks of newborn-sized clothes. She couldn't wait to find out whether she'd be buying boys' or girls' clothes. But her shopping trip wasn't going to last long.

"My back is really starting to hurt," Jennifer told her aunt.

What she didn't realize was the labour had already begun.

"Let's get you home," said Aunt June.

Every bump along the short trip home brought sharp pains in Jennifer's lower back. Enough pain to nearly take her breath away.

"I don't think it's labour," she told her aunt. "It's all in my back."

Jennifer went home and napped for a couple of hours. At home, she was overcome with exhaustion. The cramping in her back started up once more.

Lying on the couch, she was starting to worry something might be wrong, when suddenly she wanted to throw up. She managed to make it to the toilet. The last thing she needed this night was to be cleaning up vomit.

But the nausea confirmed it was time to call the doctor.

"Nelson, give me the paper with the doctor's number, would you?"

Her fingers were shaking as she dialled the number. She got the answering machine.

"The message says he's at the clinic tonight," she said. "I don't have a choice, Nelson. I have to walk down there."

In her exhaustion and pain, Jennifer managed to make the five-minute walk down to the medical clinic. She was relieved to see the lights on in Dr. Kent's office.

"Get her onto the table right away," Dr. Kent told the nurse.

Jennifer let herself relax on the table. Part of her was excited about the possibility she would soon see her children. Another part of her was scared that something was seriously wrong.

"Five centimetres," said Dr. Kent. "I can't believe you walked over here. I knew we should have kept you in the hospital."

Nelson was sitting in the chair in front of Dr. Kent's desk. "Nelson, go out to the pay phone and call a cab right away. There's no time to waste here."

Meanwhile, Dr. Kent called the hospital to ensure everything was ready for Jennifer's arrival.

As Jennifer listened to him speaking to the hospital staff, she knew everything was going as planned. Her new family was just moments away.

Dr. Kent hung up the phone. "Everything's going to be fine, Jennifer," he said. "Hopefully the cab won't be much longer. Stay right here until it arrives."

Dr. Kent opened the door to his office into the lobby.

"Is the taxi on the way?" he yelled to Nelson.

Jennifer couldn't hear Nelson's response, but there was no mistaking Dr. Kent's response. He was furious.

"What are you doing out there? I told you to call a taxi! This is not a joke! She has to get to the hospital now!"

Dr. Kent's nurse helped Jennifer off the table and to get her clothes on.

The pain was getting more intense, and it was getting harder for Jennifer to move.

She managed to get her coat and boots back on, and they began the walk to the clinic entrance.

"Please God let the taxi be here," she heard Dr. Kent say to the nurse.

When Jennifer walked through the doors, Nelson was standing outside. Two women were getting into their car. When they looked at Jennifer and realized her situation, they asked if she was okay.

"I'm on the way to the hospital to have my babies as soon as the taxi gets here," said Jennifer.

"You're in labour!" said the first woman. "Well, there's no way you'll be waiting for a taxi. Get in." So Nelson and Jennifer climbed into the back seat. Jennifer was grateful that at least she would be at the hospital in just a few minutes.

The pain, compounded with her anxiety and excitement, made the ride feel as though it were taking forever. But soon they were getting out of the car in front of the emergency doors.

"Are you Jennifer?" asked the nurse. She was standing at the entrance with a wheelchair, ready to take Jennifer to the operating room. "Well, don't worry. Everything is all ready for you. Just have a seat and you'll be well taken care of."

With that, the nurse headed down the hallway.

She looked behind her to see if Nelson was with them. She wasn't the least bit surprised when she saw him wandering off down a corridor in the opposite direction. No longer did she care. All that mattered now were these children.

17

"Do you need anything for the pain?" asked the nurse.

"The babies . . ." Jennifer managed to utter from her groggy state.

She had to ask herself whether or not she was dreaming.

"You've had a bit of a reaction to the anaesthetic," replied the nurse. "The girls are fine, but it's very important you rest."

"Nelson?" Jennifer could hear his voice, but she couldn't see him.

"Everybody out," she heard a female voice say.

Then her world went dark once again.

18

It was morning.

That much Jennifer understood. She was surrounded by the smells of toast and bacon, but there was only one thing she wanted at that moment.

She rang for the nurse.

"Did you say I have girls? Are they okay? When can I see them?"

"They're just fine, Jennifer, we'll bring them in right away," said the nurse. "She's awake," the nurse called out as she left the room.

Jennifer tried to sit up. She was so anxious to see her daughters. But she quickly realized that a Caesarean section was major surgery. Her stomach was pulled tight, and it was impossible to move.

Suddenly, the first little bed appeared from around the corner, and Jennifer started to cry. She was about to meet her daughters for the first time.

"Do you need anything for pain?" asked the nurse.

Jennifer had no words. She certainly felt no pain at the moment.

They were perfect.

"You have two beautiful girls there," said the smiling nurse.

Two little girls with a healthy body weight and both with beautiful dark hair. They were wearing yellow hospital pyjamas.

"Please don't try to get up yet," the nurse instructed Jennifer. "I'll put the girls on your chest. Just relax."

It was a moment like no other. Their warm little bodies felt so right against Jennifer's skin. She couldn't wait to begin taking care of them.

"I want to put their own pyjamas on them," Jennifer told the nurse.

The nurse giggled at Jennifer's eagerness. "Let's get you up and on the mend first, okay?"

The next morning, there was no stopping Jennifer.

She could manage to stand nearly upright. It was uncomfortable, but it was just enough to change the girls' diapers and get them into their own clothes.

Despite her pain from the surgery, Jennifer was also the first to give them baths later that afternoon.

"Beautiful girls you have there, Jennifer," said Dr. Kent.

Jennifer looked up. He was just walking into the room as she was drying one of the girls off from her bath.

"They are," she said, smiling with pride. "Has Nelson seen them?"

"He was here for their birth and watched from behind a curtain," said Dr. Kent. "I'm sure he's as proud as you. He also called wanting to speak to you yesterday, but it didn't make much sense to me. Nelson wanted to know if I would release you from the hospital so you could get a PIN number assigned to a new bank card," explained her doctor.

"You weren't even awake. I hope you're not offended, but I asked him if he was crazy. You've been through a lot, and that bank card isn't something you need to worry about."

For the next five days, Jennifer didn't worry about much at all. It was the best time of her life. Nelson didn't bother to visit, but he did continue to call.

And his reason for calling was always the same. "When are you coming home?" he'd say. "I'm having seizures. I need your help."

Jennifer had a private room at the hospital. It was just her and the girls, with help from the hospital staff. It was a good time, and she was enjoying the peace and quiet.

On Tuesday morning, a nurse asked her a question that, until then, she hadn't even considered.

"We can't keep calling them Baby Hart One and Two," said the nurse. "Do you have any names in mind?"

"No, I don't," said Jennifer. "But I think Karen and Krista sound nice."

And there was no more to consider. Karen and Krista Hart it would be.

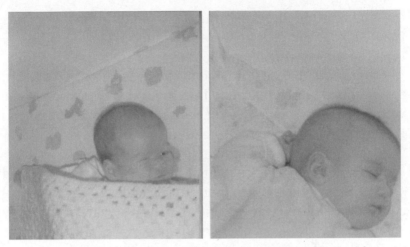

*Krista and Karen Hart when they were just days old.
Photos by Jennifer Hicks.*

19

A week later, Jennifer was finally allowed to bring her children home. She got up that morning, gave them their baths, and dressed them in their little pink jogging suits. She still had a lot of pain from the surgery, and standing up was quite difficult, but she wasn't about to let that stop her.

Today would be the day they would finally have their own bed in their own home. Jennifer was excited, and she had plenty to do before Nelson and his aunt Lucy came to pick her up this afternoon.

The first thing she had to conquer was the mountain of gifts that had been donated to her and the girls. The town of Gander had proven its generosity on many occasions in the past, and she was surprised at how supportive people actually were.

Stacked in the corner were boxes of formula, diapers, clothes, and other necessities. All were donated by people who wanted to make sure the twins had a good start in life.

She continued getting the girls ready until it was nap time. She had an hour or so before lunch was served, so she took the time to relax herself.

Lying on the hospital bed, she was looking forward to her own blankets and pillows. At the same time, she wondered how Nelson would be, now that life had changed considerably and the twins needed so much care.

It didn't take long before she got her answers.

"I can't believe we're going home." Jennifer nearly cried as she dressed the girls in their little jackets. March was still considered mid-winter in Gander, and she wasn't taking any chances. She snuggled them in blankets and put them into their respective baskets, while Nelson and his aunt Lucy watched on.

They were ready for the car.

Lucy grabbed Karen, while Jennifer carried Krista. Nelson walked slightly ahead of them. The twins were born a healthy size. Karen weighed in at five pounds and eight ounces, and Krista weighted seven pounds.

For Jennifer, those seven pounds felt a lot heavier as she tried to navigate the hospital hallways with the heavy basket. With each step she felt like the six-inch scar from her surgery was pulling apart.

When they finally made it to the front entrance of the hospital, Aunt Lucy walked to the parking lot to get the car. When she arrived back at the main door, she quickly hopped out from behind the wheel to help Jennifer. They both put the girls into their car seats. Nelson was already in the front passenger seat and hadn't said a word.

Jennifer knew he hadn't been entirely excited about the girls, but she wasn't expecting him to be so cold.

At the apartment building, Nelson was out of the car and up the stairs before Aunt Lucy had the ignition turned off.

Between the two women, they carried the babies and

all the supplies up the stairs and into the apartment. It took several trips back and forth to the car, and Jennifer could feel the incision was starting to hurt from the strain. But there was work to be done, and she was too excited to let a little bit of pain prevent her from enjoying bringing her babies home.

"Will you be okay now?" asked Aunt Lucy.

"I'll be fine. I just need to get the girls into their crib, and then we will all be getting a good night's sleep," replied Jennifer.

Aunt Lucy left Jennifer and the two children, and Nelson was already in front of the television.

"Help me bring the girls into the room," said Jennifer. "My surgery is beginning to burn. I really think I've overdone it today."

All the gifts, diapers, and clothes were stacked by the door, and Jennifer knew it was just as well to get it packed away in the bedroom. Nelson picked up the basket with little Krista and brought her into the bedroom. Jennifer followed with Karen, and her eyes shot open with shock when she walked into the bedroom. Jennifer felt like all her questions about Nelson were answered.

He simply wasn't interested.

In a box in a corner of the bedroom was the girls' crib. He hadn't even attempted to open it while she was in the hospital.

She was sick, tired, excited, and happier than she had ever been in her life. Yet she stood in the doorway of the bedroom looking down at the unopened box with tears in her eyes.

He didn't care.

So instead of getting ready for bed, Jennifer mixed several bottles of formula for the girls and arranged them in the refrigerator so that she was ready for the endless feedings she would face through this night. She made a suitable changing area in the room with diapers and wipes so everything was readily accessible.

Then she quietly took a knife out of the kitchen drawer and opened the crib box.

There seemed to be a thousand pieces and endless instructions.

The tears were coming again. The channels changed in the living room.

The girls were hungry again. They were always hungry, it seemed.

What is wrong? thought Jennifer. *This damn infant formula just isn't satisfying them.*

After the feeding, she went back to assembling the crib.

"What is wrong with you, my son! Can't you get off that couch to do anything?" She yelled at Nelson for being so irresponsible, but at the same time she knew it was useless. Her screams fell on deaf ears, so she continued on.

By nine o'clock that night the girls were finally lying in their crib. She had only bought one, because they would be moving to a new apartment soon. She just prayed she had done a good enough job and that the thing wouldn't fall apart in the night, sending the girls crashing to the floor.

When they get their own room, I'll have another crib to put together, she thought.

Once Jennifer finally got to bed that night, she was beyond exhausted. She was also sore, and sad, but that didn't stop her from falling into a deep sleep immediately.

"Where am I?" She sat up abruptly from her sleep. One of the babies was crying, and she realized she had been asleep for quite some time.

The pain from her incision quickly reminded her of where she was. The clock indicated Jennifer had been asleep for two hours, and Karen and Krista were hungry again. Nelson was lying next to her.

When she tried to stand, the pain from her cut

intensified. But without a word to Nelson, she went to the refrigerator and made another two bottles of formula.

She took turns feeding and burping them both and went back to sleep.

An hour later, she was awake again. They wanted more food.

For the next twenty-four hours she would wake only to feed and change her babies. She did it all without any help from Nelson.

20

The application to Newfoundland and Labrador Housing had already been approved.

In a few weeks the family would be moving to a housing unit where the girls would finally have their own bedroom. Both Jennifer and Nelson were looking forward to having their own space, but Jennifer was hoping that the move would also lighten the bills. Lately it seemed the money was running out too quickly after payday. She didn't see the welfare cheques. They belonged to Nelson. On payday he would pick up groceries and pay the bills, and Jennifer was glad that was one less chore she had to worry about. The only time Jennifer saw cash was when she would get her family allowance cheque.

"Nelson! I need money for diapers," Jennifer called out. She could hear him getting up off the couch and rustling through the closet. She was down to two diapers and Nelson was headed out, for God knew where, or how long.

"I don't have any money," he said.

"What do you mean? We just got our cheque! What did you do with it?"

Nelson was going to the bar more often these days. She wasn't sure if he was alone or with his mother, but she suspected he was spending more time playing the slots, a habit for which their meagre income from social services didn't make room.

"Well? I need diapers, so figure something out," she snapped.

Nelson left and came back soon after with diapers. "I borrowed the money from Mom," he said. "But these girls are getting too expensive. If I gets that settlement from insurance, I won't have to worry anymore."

Discussions had already begun between lawyers and the insurance company on a settlement from the car accident, and Nelson was anxious for his hearing.

"I'm sick of trying to buy everything," Jennifer pleaded. "You're not giving me enough money to pay for the things I need for the girls. This is going to have to change, and I can't wait for you to get a settlement that you don't even know you'll win yet."

Jennifer was well on her way to recovering from the operation, and the girls were now two months old.

She was getting a little more sleep at night, thanks to a change in the girls' diets. Though her family doctor didn't approve, Jennifer was convinced the infant formula wasn't agreeing with the babies' bellies, so she took things into her own hands. One morning, after a particularly restless night, she washed the formula down the drain.

"This formula just isn't satisfying them," Jennifer said. "If I don't change their milk, I'll never get another night's sleep again."

From then on, Karen and Krista went on a diet of Carnation condensed milk mixed with water. Dr. McDonald wasn't impressed with Jennifer's decision. But she was right in that it did wonders for the girls' sleep. Finally, she began getting more rest.

She was starting to handle her day-to-day chores a little better, too. Nelson's new medication seemed to have brought his grand mal seizures under control for several months now. The grand mal seizures had been particularly tough on Jennifer, as well as Nelson. He would fall to the floor, shaking uncontrollably, and there were many times Jennifer wondered how he had come out of it without seriously hurting himself.

But with the new medication, she also had the added responsibility of making sure he was taking it. As a result, in addition to taking care of the children, she now had to monitor his medication twice a day.

And there were still plenty of petit mal seizures. He'd stand there, usually patting his stomach, his head making odd jerking movements. The partial seizures were harder to identify. In fact, sometimes in the middle of a seizure, he could respond to questions and still communicate.

But many of the partial seizures had gone unnoticed these days. Nelson was either lying on the couch, asleep, or gone out most of the time. And with newborn twins, Jennifer was busy every second of the day.

Nelson and Jennifer's house on Bennett Avenue in Gander. The couple moved in here when their daughters were just three months old. Photo by Colleen Lewis.

21

Finally. Moving day.

For the past several weeks, Jennifer had begun packing the contents of the entire apartment. She labelled everything and sorted items that would be moved first. There was no help from Nelson, and at this point she didn't expect any.

She had gathered up the boxes, which were marked according to the items the girls would need first. Then she took apart the crib. Piece by piece, she carried everything down to the car. Then, one box at a time, she brought everything she needed to their new house on Bennett Avenue.

"This is quite the change from that small apartment," said her sister Penny.

Penny had spent the afternoon putting together the cribs and helping Jennifer to unpack.

"Sure is. It's going to be nice to have my own laundry room. You wouldn't believe how much clothes I have to wash in the run of a day," said Jennifer. "It's never-ending. Plus, I have a feeling they are going to like having their own separate cribs. They're getting so big these days, there's not much room for the two of them in one crib anymore. I can't wait to decorate their room. It's also going to be nice not have to step over boxes of diapers to get to my bed," she laughed.

That evening the two sisters finished unpacking, and Penny helped put the girls to bed for their first night in the new house.

"What time do you expect Nelson?" asked Penny.

"I don't know," said Jennifer. "I'm not worried, anyway. He doesn't do anything while he's here. The only time he's got anything to say is when the girls are asleep, and then all he wants to do is argue."

"I've noticed he doesn't play with the girls much," said Penny. "Is everything okay?"

Jennifer ignored the question. She didn't feel like talking about it at all, and she certainly didn't know how to explain it.

"Well, I'll stay here tonight. Just in case you need some more help," said Penny. "Tomorrow my neighbour will be over, and he'll give you a hand getting the rest of the furniture in."

It took a week or so, but Jennifer finally got the girls settled into the house. She did most of the work, but was grateful for the ongoing help from her sister. Even after everything had been moved in, there were endless chores to be done.

"I need to run up to the store to pick up a few things," said Penny one afternoon while she and her husband were visiting. "Come on, Jennifer, you've been working too hard lately. Let's go have some girl time."

"Yes, we can look after the girls," said Penny's husband.

But Jennifer had never left Karen and Krista alone with their father before, and she wasn't sure if it was a good idea.

"I don't know," said Jennifer. "What do you think, Nelson?"

"Oh, he can handle them for half an hour or so," said Penny, not giving Nelson a chance to respond. She handed Jennifer her coat and the two headed out the door.

They made the short drive to the local grocery store, and Penny was stocking up on cans of soup when she asked Jennifer, "What's the problem with Nelson and the girls? I don't see him ever pick them up or feed or change them. Is it only when we're around, or is he like that all the time?"

"I don't understand it either," said Jennifer. "Sometimes it's like he needs more attention than they do. It's like he's getting mad at me for taking care of them. I can tell by the look on his face. To be honest, I think he believes the girls should be able to take care of themselves even though they're only three months old."

Jennifer put a few items in her cart but then got an uneasy feeling.

"Speaking of Nelson, it's time to go back. I don't really want to be away from the girls for too long."

When they got back to the house, Jennifer could hear the babies crying before she even opened the door.

When she walked into the apartment, Nelson was sitting on the couch and the girls were both crying in their playpen. And it was no wonder they were upset. Karen and Krista were in desperate need of a diaper change.

"You couldn't change their shitty diaper," Jennifer yelled at Nelson.

"I'm not changing them. That's your job," he snapped back.

Penny and her neighbour left while Jennifer cleaned up the girls and started getting ready for supper. But it wasn't long before the girls were crying again. This time they wanted food.

Jennifer mixed their bottles of Carnation milk and was feeding Krista first while Karen anxiously waited for her turn.

"Why aren't you starting supper?" Nelson asked. "I'm starved, and would ya hurry up and feed Karen? She's getting on my nerves!"

"Can't you see I'm busy? You're going to have to wait, Nelson."

"Very good. I think you care about those youngsters more than me."

22

Jennifer's surgery had completely healed by that spring, and she was longing to get outside and enjoy some fresh air.

"Well, my dear, dress them up and we'll go out for a walk." It was Nelson's mother.

Jennifer caught the look on Nelson's face. She knew he did not want her to go out and enjoy her time with the girls, but she didn't care. By now she had come to realize Nelson wanted her undivided attention, but there were times when the demands were simply too much.

It was a beautiful Saturday morning, and Jennifer had just bought a second-hand stroller for the twins. She didn't have a chance to try out the stroller yet, mainly because it wasn't easy to get out with two babies and no help. Today she was pleased to have some help, and she wasn't about to miss this opportunity.

"We'll only be gone for half an hour so, Nelson," said Jennifer. There was no reply, but she didn't care how cranky he was.

She dressed the girls up so they were looking their best, and they headed out the door. The women made sure the two little girls were safely in the stroller seats.

"Let's cross the road to the sidewalk," suggested Jennifer. "It will be easier walking there until I get used to the stroller and the girls' weight."

But as she pushed the stroller up onto the sidewalk, she got the scare of a lifetime. The wheel of the stroller fell off. She could barely handle the weight, and she felt both lucky and relieved when Nelson's mother reached in quickly to make sure the girls were safe.

Jennifer's heart was pounding in her chest. She felt a wave of heat come over her and wondered if she wasn't about to pass out from the fright.

When she regained her strength, her one free hand was beneath the stroller holding the weight of the girls.

Struggling, they managed to get the stroller back across the road and to get the girls out of their straps and into the house.

"Oh my God," Jennifer said. She was still out of breath from the whole ordeal. "I can't believe how lucky we are the girls didn't get hurt."

Once the girls were safe in their playpen, Nelson's mother went home. For that Jennifer was grateful, because she couldn't handle another fight between Nelson and his mother at the moment. Those arguments just seemed to be escalating more often these days, and most of the time for reasons that didn't make sense to Jennifer at all. The last one was over the fact she didn't like Nelson's jeans. The two of them would argue endlessly for the dumbest reasons.

Jennifer poured herself a cup of tea and sat next to the playpen.

"I guess I'm going to have to call the people who sold me that stroller," said Jennifer. "My girls could have been killed out there today."

"I broke the wheel," said Nelson.

Jennifer could hardly believe what she was hearing. He flicked through the channels.

"Yes, I'm sure you did," Jennifer said sarcastically. "Why did you do that, Nelson?"

"You don't need to be taking them youngsters out of the house. You can stay here with them," he told her.

She put her tea down, realizing he was serious. He had done it.

"Are you serious?" She stood up. Jennifer was raised not to swear, but the curse words rolled off her tongue. "You son of bitch. You could have killed those girls. Do you know how serious this is? What the fuck is wrong with you, my son?" she screamed.

But Nelson simply ignored her, continuing to flick through the channels.

"I don't have to put up with this," she yelled. "I wouldn't have any problem raising those girls on my own."

Frustrated with his lack of response, Jennifer walked into her bedroom. She knew the situation was not good. Deep down she knew the right thing to do was to leave the father of her children. Her hopes of having the perfect family were quickly diminishing. This wasn't going to work. But at the moment there were bigger things to worry about.

Karen was the first to start crying. Jennifer went out to the fridge and started mixing bottles. Meanwhile, Krista needed to be changed. She tended to her daughters, although she was exhausted from the events of this day. She lay down for a nap, and when she woke several hours later, Nelson was nowhere to be seen.

She fed and bathed the children, and then the three went to bed for the night.

When she woke the next morning, Nelson was already out of the bed. She had gotten up in the middle of the night, so she knew he had slept at home, but where was he now?

Eventually she summoned the energy to walk out into the kitchen, where there was a plastic rose sitting in a vase on the table. From the dollar store, she suspected, but it was still a nice gesture. Shortly after, he came in with some takeout breakfast, and Jennifer was grateful not to have to cook.

She put the events of yesterday behind her and forged ahead for another day.

Another day to make things right for her daughters.

23

Jennifer sat at the table, feeding Karen and staring at the plastic rose. She wondered where Nelson was today. It seemed he was never home these days, and she needed him.

He had the money from their monthly welfare cheque. In fact, Jennifer hadn't been shopping in months. When Nelson got paid, he would volunteer to go pick up groceries. But this month, the few bags of groceries he brought home weren't nearly enough.

There were three diapers left in the box, and they would soon disappear.

And as Karen's little lips sucked down the last of her milk, Jennifer was worried about where she would get the next can of milk.

Would Nelson get home in time to go the store? Was there even any money left?

Jennifer was finishing up the feeding when she took a sudden cramp in her belly. She recognized at once what it was. She had started her period. But these days her periods presented a whole new problem. With barely enough money for diapers, there was never enough for a box of tampons. So Jennifer had to learn to make do. She went to the cupboard where she had stored a pile of plastic bags and old rags that she had saved up. With those two items she had learned to make her own sanitary napkins. It would have to suffice, no matter how uncomfortable it was.

Two hours later, Nelson came home.

"Where were you?" she asked.

"At the bar."

"I'm down to the last diaper, and there's no milk for the girls. You have to go to the store right away."

"I don't have any money," he snapped. "I don't know what you're going to do. Wait till you get the family allowance cheque, I suppose."

"There's no way. I need those things now, even if I have to call the welfare office," she said.

"I don't care what you do," he said. And Nelson headed back out the door.

Jennifer picked up the phone and called the local Salvation Army food bank and explained her situation.

"We'll be right there," said Captain Budgell.

The captain and his wife arrived within an hour. They sat with Jennifer and talked to her about how things were going, and they spent some time playing with the girls.

But then it was down to business.

"Can we have a look at your cupboards to see what kinds of items you need?" he asked.

When the officer opened the cupboards and the refrigerator, it didn't take long for him to evaluate the need.

Jennifer and the babies needed everything. There was no food. No diapers.

"We'll be back in a couple of hours, Jennifer," Captain Budgell said. "And we'll be making sure that you and your girls will be okay."

Jennifer felt like the weight of the world had been lifted from her shoulders. Finally, there was someone to take care of her and her daughters. She was so relieved.

But she also wondered what Nelson was doing with the rest of the money. And where was he getting his food? She imagined that while she and the girls had bare cupboards, Nelson was treating himself to takeout pizza and fried chicken. The picture was also becoming clearer that Nelson had a gambling problem.

When the Salvation Army officers came back that day, they brought over $600 in food and toiletries. There was even baby shampoo and soaps for the girls.

For the next little while she could relax without having to worry about how she would pay for the needs of her children.

24

Jennifer was feeling a lot more relaxed with plenty of food on hand. For the past few days she and the girls were better able to enjoy their time together. Especially with full bellies. This morning, she was up and made a breakfast of sausage, eggs, and toast. Now she was enjoying her second cup of tea of the morning.

Nelson, meanwhile, had been in the shower for the last half-hour and had been in an unusually good mood all morning.

Just as Jennifer started in on the dishes, he came out dressed and ready for the day.

"I'm leaving now, I'll be back later today," he announced as he put on his shoes.

Jennifer was getting used to his absence. In many ways she enjoyed it when he wasn't around. Especially at times like these, when she had everything she needed for the girls.

Nelson had fixed the stroller for her, and she spent most of the day out walking, and even did a little bit of visiting with the neighbours.

After supper, she got the girls ready for bed and sat back to watch some television. It seemed like it had been months since she'd had time to watch her favourite shows. Just as she was getting comfortable, she saw the beams of Nelson's headlights shine across the living room wall. He was home, and the last thing she wanted now was another argument.

Instead, he came through the door like an excited boy who had big news.

And he did have big news. In his hand was a brown envelope.

"Wait till you see this, Jennifer," he announced.

In the envelope was a cheque for $28,000.

"I told you I'd get the settlement. I didn't need any lawyers. I went to Grand Falls today and settled my insurance claim with the company. They gave me the money right there," he boasted.

"Nelson, you know what the welfare told you about this,

right? The money has to be turned in to the welfare office or they're going to cut us off," said Jennifer.

"This is my money. I'm the one who got beat up in that accident, and the welfare can't take this from me," he snapped back.

"I need money to feed the children. Either you give the money to the welfare or you have to use it to pay the bills here," Jennifer explained.

"I'm not giving you one dime," he said. "This is my money. You can go to the welfare to get your own money or live off the family allowance."

Jennifer knew that if Nelson kept the money there would be no money coming from welfare for her to take care of the kids. But there was no changing his mind.

He kept the money without reporting it.

When there was no welfare cheque in the mail that first month, Nelson realized he was being backed into a corner.

"Lets go shopping," he said.

It was obvious Nelson had some sort of plan, and Jennifer couldn't see any other way out. So she followed along. They headed out to the local furniture store, and before she knew it their house was filled with the finest furniture around. Jennifer had actually lost track of how much they had spent.

"I'll just tell the welfare I spent all the money. Then they'll be forced to give us back our cheques," said Nelson.

But, as Jennifer expected, it didn't work out that way.

They were going to have to sell the furniture and live off that, the welfare officer told Jennifer as she pleaded for money. Then, as quickly as the furniture had arrived, it began to disappear. They were forced to sell it all before they would be allowed back on social services. Piece by piece, all the wonderful furniture was bought and taken from the house.

Nelson collected the money, and Jennifer was left with no settlement money, and no income.

"I don't know what he's done with the money, but I need to feed my kids," Jennifer pleaded again with her caseworker.

"We're sorry, but Nelson was supposed to turn in that cheque," the worker explained. "Without the cheque, we can't give you any money."

"Well, if you aren't going to help me, I will get the police involved. I don't know what Nelson did with the money, but me and the girls need money to survive," said Jennifer.

Jennifer left the office and called the police to tell them her situation. An RCMP officer went back to the social worker with Jennifer, and shortly after that they reinstated her income.

25

Although the girls were only four months old, Jennifer had already figured out she did not want any more children with Nelson.

"Is this your decision, or his?" asked her family doctor.

But it was completely Jennifer's decision. Nelson wasn't the caring father she had hoped he would be.

The final straw for her was just the other day, when she was feeding Karen. She usually fed the girls half an hour apart, but for some reason Krista had woken up in the crib a little early.

With Krista feeding in her lap, and Karen crying from the bedroom, Jennifer called Nelson. "Why don't you go pick up Karen for a few minutes?"

Nelson walked around the corner and screamed, "Shut up!" Suddenly there was a loud bang, and Jennifer feared the worst. She jumped up and looked down the hallway. Nelson walked toward her and left the apartment.

Her heart was pounding as she approached the bedroom door. She was afraid of what he might have done. Slowly, she entered the room and looked around to discover that he had kicked a hole completely through the door.

That was enough. The next morning, she made an appointment with Dr. McDonald.

"It's my choice, and I don't want any more youngsters," she explained to him.

It took some convincing, but her doctor finally agreed with her and booked the appointment for surgery.

For the next couple weeks, all Jennifer could think of was the surgery. In particular, she wondered how the housework would get done with her being laid up for weeks. As usual, she began doing the prep work well in advance.

A couple weeks later, and she was nearly ready. Nelson had already made it clear he wouldn't be taking care of the girls, so she had to find a sitter. Fortunately, her neighbour Sheila would be able to help, and Jennifer trusted her with the girls.

"Thanks for doing this, Sheila," said Jennifer as she brought the girls into her neighbour's house.

Her surgery was scheduled for 8:00 a.m., so she brought the girls to the sitter the night before. She prepared their beds and had everything from bottles to diapers ready for Sheila.

At home she had taken care of all the housework except for two loads of laundry. She left the baskets sitting on the couch with the portions of detergent already measured out. All Nelson would have to do was bring the clothes downstairs and put it in the washer. With two babies, there was no room for a break in the housework. Things piled up quickly.

She went home expecting a full night's sleep without the twins to keep her awake. But being away from them wasn't easy. It seemed like she was awake every five minutes.

Jennifer was out of bed and ready for surgery well ahead of time.

At the hospital, her surgery went well, but she wasn't released until late in the afternoon. It was later than she had expected, and Nelson was there to pick her up.

"Let's go," he said. They were still in Jennifer's hospital room, and she was sitting on the edge of the bed.

"Um, she isn't walking anywhere," said the nurse, who was giving Jennifer her instructions to care for the incision.

"Why not?" questioned Nelson.

"She isn't able to walk, and she isn't able to lift anything heavy for the next six weeks. For the next few days she shouldn't lift anything at all, and she should get plenty of rest. Nelson, you will have to help her with the babies, or she could seriously injure herself."

The nurse went outside to get a wheelchair and then helped Jennifer get seated.

Nelson went on ahead, and by the time they made it downstairs he was outside with the car. The nurse helped Jennifer into the car while Nelson sat behind the wheel. Jennifer could see the frustrated look on the nurse's face.

At Sheila's, Jennifer got out of the car to gather up their girls and their belongings. She looked behind to see Nelson still seating in his seat.

"Aren't you going to help me, my son?" she asked.

"You can go get them."

Jennifer went into the house, where the girls were playing happily on a blanket on the living room floor.

"Is Nelson helping?" asked Sheila.

Jennifer didn't say anything. She just went to work and gathered up the girls' belongings. She had hoped Nelson would take some pity on her and lend a hand, but she ended up bringing everything to the car. The playpen was the heaviest load, so she brought that out first. Then she went back and brought the girls out to the car, one at a time.

By the time they got home, Jennifer was exhausted. But there was still work to be done, despite her aching body. She put the girls into their cribs and unpacked their diaper bags. Nelson quickly disappeared to a friend's house in order to help him work on his car for the town's upcoming annual derby.

It was all just another reminder to Jennifer that not having any more children was the right decision.

Jennifer had been so busy with the girls she hadn't noticed that the laundry was still sitting where she had left it last night. There was no way she was leaving it there for another night.

She attempted to lift the basket, but the pain was unbearable. So she kicked it over so that the pile of clothes was on the floor. Then, using her feet, she kicked the pile across the floor and down over the stairs. At first she thought she could manage the steps, but her cut was burning. She knew she'd already done too much this evening, but if she could just get the clothes washed and into the dryer, she'd be content. So she sat on the top step for a few minutes. Then, slowly, she lowered herself to the next step, and so on. Finally, she reached the bottom step and put each piece of clothing into the washer. She was in agony, but there was no turning back. She managed to crawl back up over the steps, but again she took a break on the main floor.

As she sat with her back to the wall, she thought to herself, *I could have bled to death on these stairs tonight, and no one would have known. And I don't think Nelson would have cared.*

26

Nelson wasn't the partner or father Jennifer had hoped for. But she never gave up on the idea of having the perfect family for her girls. They deserved it.

But there was one more thing she needed to complete her family.

"You know, Nelson, I wonder what the girls will think as they grow up and realize that my last name is Hicks, and yours is Hart?" Jennifer asked. "How do we explain that to them? That's not the way it's supposed to be."

As he always did, whenever she brought up marriage, Nelson found a reason to leave the room. It was a scenario that played out many times for Jennifer for months, so she was astounded when Nelson finally decided to propose one day that winter. There wasn't anything romantic. In fact, Jennifer could barely recall how he had asked, but she was glad he did. For her, this was the first step in becoming a real family.

"Who will you invite?" asked Jennifer. "We've got plenty of relatives who'll want to go."

"There won't be any invitations," he said. "We'll be getting married at the courthouse, or we won't be getting married at all."

It wasn't what Jennifer wanted to hear. The girls would be having their first birthday in a month, and Nelson was clear. He wanted the wedding done and over with before then.

"I would like to have a wedding dress and get married in a church," Jennifer protested. "Why can't we wait till the girls are a little bit older? Imagine how beautiful they would look as flower girls."

"Well, that's not the way it's going to be, and there isn't enough money for a dress, either," said Nelson.

Nelson's attitude toward getting married made it difficult for Jennifer to get excited about the ceremony. To her that's all it would be, a ceremony. They certainly weren't planning anything special, let alone spectacular.

One would expect the big day would approach quickly with so many things to do, but for Jennifer the day came upon her like any other. However, there were important details she was concerned about. She wanted to look good, and she had no idea what she would wear.

Perhaps the dress she had worn to Susan's wedding? She pulled the dress down from the closet, noticing that it looked frayed and aged. But it would have to do.

She pulled the dress up around her hips and realized there was no way this was going to work. The dress was simply too small.

"What am I going to do?" she asked Susan. "Nelson isn't going to give me any money, and the only thing that I have in my closet that's respectable is way too small."

"Come on over, let's see what I have," Susan said. Jennifer prayed there would be something in her sister's closet.

She pulled out a dress Jennifer had seen Susan wear many times before. Jennifer knew as soon as she looked at the dress that it wouldn't fit, either. She tried it on, as a last hope, but no matter how badly she wanted it to fit, there was just no way.

"That's the only dress I have," said Susan. "I'm sorry, Jennifer."

The day of her wedding didn't exceed her expectations, and it didn't even meet them. It was a day much like any other.

She got up, fed and bathed the girls, and did her chores as usual. She took some extra time with her makeup and hair, but she left the house wearing her best jeans and T-shirt. Even her best jeans weren't a good pair, but she refused to be sad on what was supposed to be one of the happiest days of her life.

Susan was already at the courthouse when she got there. Her three beautiful nieces were there as well.

At least I've got my family here, she thought.

They walked into the judge's office, and Jennifer was the first to sign the legal document. Then Nelson.

They were married. It was as simple as that. There was no honeymoon. The next morning was the same as any other. She was feeding the girls breakfast when Nelson called out.

"I need my black T-shirt!"

"Give me a minute. Karen needs something to drink," Jennifer replied.

"You're my wife now," he said. "And you'll do what I want, when I want."

Jennifer got the T-shirt without a word, and Nelson got dressed. She sat at the table with the girls, and in her mind she could hardly believe he had said those words. They hadn't been married for twenty-four hours, and he was clear, she was now his.

As Nelson was putting on his shoes, he made an announcement.

"I'm going and I won't be back."

"Where the hell are you going, my son?" she asked. He left the apartment without giving her an answer.

Jennifer was stunned by the change in him, but she was happy to see him leave the house that morning. Initially she believed he wouldn't be gone long. With the girls' birthday just three days away, she had plenty to keep her busy without him being around with his own demands. But she also needed money, and Nelson had taken that with him, of course.

Afternoon came and went, with still no sign of Nelson, which wasn't uncommon these days. Jennifer believed he was spending more and more time playing the slot machines at the bar.

But when he failed to show up that night, she started to worry.

She was worried he might have had a seizure, or something might have happened to him. But she had plenty more than Nelson to worry about.

The cupboards were empty. There were only a handful of diapers left in the box.

She also needed to buy something for the girls' birthday, and of course birthdays came with extra expenses. Even though gifts and cake were out of the question, she needed the money that was in Nelson's pocket. She longed to give them the birthday they deserved.

But another night passed, and Jennifer was starting to believe that the man she had married two days ago had abandoned them.

"I don't know where to turn," Jennifer told Mervin on the phone. Mervin was Nelson's brother. Unlike Nelson, he was worried about Jennifer and the kids. There were many times Jennifer could only wonder why Nelson wasn't more like his brother. Mervin loved his children and was a good provider for his family.

"I've called around, and it seems like no one has seen him since the wedding."

"Well, if he isn't home tonight, I'll make sure you and the girls are okay," he said.

Jennifer was relieved. At least Mervin could drive her to the food bank, and perhaps even lend her the money for diapers.

As she feared, Nelson didn't come home for the third night.

The next morning, she called Mervin again.

"Don't worry about it," he said. "Just give me a couple of hours and we'll be down to give the girls a birthday party. I don't know what the hell is wrong with my brother. He isn't thinking of anyone but himself."

Mervin showed up that evening with a birthday cake and a meal of fried chicken. He had gifts for each of the girls.

"You really saved the girls' birthday," Jennifer told him. "Thanks again, Mervin, you've been so good to us. We've certainly needed plenty of help from you over the past year."

The day ended on a happy note, but Jennifer couldn't get to sleep. For the fourth night there was no word from Nelson.

Two days later, he strolled into the apartment like nothing had ever happened.

"Where the hell were you?"

"I was in Quebec."

That was all Nelson would say that day. Jennifer screamed at him to find out why he had left, but he simply walked away.

27

Nelson had promised not to do another disappearing act, but he wasn't around much, either. Jennifer was always busy with the girls, and she believed he was spending his time gambling.

The tension between him and his mother was escalating, reaching the point where they began arguing over the smallest things.

The last time she stopped by for a visit, the arguing got out of control.

"If you guys can't stop this, you're not going to be able to visit here," Jennifer said in the middle of a particularly bad argument. "I've got two youngsters here, and I don't want them listening to these rackets."

The biggest arguments usually took place later. Those were the times Nelson took out his frustrations on Jennifer.

"Why do you keep asking her over here?" asked Nelson.

"She's your mother, and if you want her to leave, you'll be the one to tell her," Jennifer said.

Jennifer was desperate for a change. So, when Nelson talked about moving into St. John's, Jennifer thought it might not be such a bad idea.

"At least in there I won't have to listen to you and your mother," she said. And deep down she was hoping the gambling would slow down as well.

It didn't take long before they had applied for public housing in St. John's and got word that their application was approved. The girls were one and a half years old when they packed up a U-Haul and made the big move 400 kilometres away to the province's capital city.

Jennifer was used to growing up in a small town, and sometimes even Gander, with a population of 10,000 people, seemed too big. She wasn't sure whether she'd like living in the city, but she was willing to give it a try.

Shortly after they passed the city limits of St. John's, they drove around the corner from a busy street to a group of several large apartment complex buildings. It seemed to her the traffic was moving ten times faster than she was used to, and there were people everywhere she looked.

As they got out of the truck in front of their building, Jennifer noticed two men smoking cigarettes over the open hood of an old truck.

But, she wasn't interested in much else at the moment than getting settled into the comfort of her own apartment. She started to move the girls' items up to their second floor, while Nelson made his way over to meet the new neighbours. It wasn't long before the two men were helping to carry their furniture and belongings up the stairs.

The new apartment was nice. It was a little bigger than she thought, and at least it had two bedrooms.

But on her first night there, Jennifer couldn't sleep. The sound of the city vibrated through the room. She couldn't stop herself from hearing the sounds of the traffic and the coming and going of neighbours all night long.

It was a long way from her quiet life in Gander, and she hoped they had made the right choice for the girls.

28

In a matter of days, they had settled in nicely. There wasn't much food in the cupboard because they had spent most of their money on the move. But Nelson had managed to land the first job Jennifer had ever known him to have.

"One of the guys next door got me the job," he announced one evening. "I'll have to work nights, but it pays pretty good.

All you need to do is tell the welfare that we're broke up, and I'll keep the money."

Jennifer looked at the girls, and then to the refrigerator she knew was nearly empty. She hoped this could be a way to a better life, where she didn't have to worry about whether or not Nelson would give her the money to buy groceries and diapers every month. She was getting tired of having to rely on the food bank once a week, and getting around in the city wasn't as easy.

Christmas would be here before long, and she wanted the extra money to make sure it was a good one for the girls.

Being alone every evening wasn't the ideal situation, but then, she was used to Nelson not being around. When he was home there were arguments, so she was happy to spend time with Karen and Krista alone. Everyone was a little happier that way.

"Hello," said Jennifer, picking up the phone.

"Hey, sister," said Susan. "How are things in the big city?"

"Great. It's a lot more hectic than Gander, but I'm getting used to it," said Jennifer. "Would you believe Nelson has a job?"

"Really? Doing what?"

"He's cleaning apartment buildings. Pretty much gone every night."

"Are you sure he isn't out spending money on those friggin' VLTs?" asked Susan. "And what about you and the girls? Is he giving you enough money to live on, or is he still taking it all for himself?"

"Well, he gives me what he can. But he says there isn't much left over from the move," said Jennifer.

"Oh, Jennifer, be careful out there," said Susan. "If you ever need anything, call me, and I'll help you any way I can. Love you."

"Love you, too, Susan. Don't worry, everything's okay."

Jennifer went back to cleaning the apartment with a

heavy heart. She missed having her family close by, and it seemed she was alone all the time now.

Fortunately, she had met a woman on the first floor whom she had grown close to, and she even offered to babysit the girls now and again. But it wasn't the same as being home. She missed having people around.

She grabbed the vacuum cleaner and headed into her bedroom to give it a good cleaning before Christmas. She wanted to clean behind the furniture, but she wasn't sure she could move it alone. Who knew when Nelson would get home? And then he probably wouldn't want to help her, anyway.

In order to move the large dresser, she decided to lessen the weight by removing each of the drawers first. She struggled to move them onto the bed.

When she finally hauled the bottom drawer out, she noticed a small brown envelope. It was thick, and she wasn't sure she even wanted to know what was in it.

But she couldn't resist. Whatever it was had been put there on purpose since they had moved in.

She pulled back the flap, revealing a stack of $100 bills. A large stack. She took them out and placed them on the bed.

One by one, she began to count, her heart beating faster with each bill she counted.

With empty cupboards, and only a few diapers left, Jennifer struggled while Nelson had kept his own money hidden. In total there was $15,000. Money he had reserved for himself.

She could no longer hold back the tears as she stared at the money in disbelief. If it wasn't for Krista, who started crying, Jennifer wasn't sure she could have moved again. She felt numb.

Her hands shook as she put the bills back into the envelope and put them back under the dresser.

What would she do? If she told Nelson, he would get mad. But how could she live in poverty while he kept the money for himself?

She didn't have long to figure out how to handle it. She heard the key in the door. Nelson was home.

He threw his jacket onto the chair and flopped himself down into his usual position on the couch. The girls were in the playpen, but he walked past them like they didn't exist.

"What's wrong with you?" he sneered.

"I only have half a dozen diapers left, and there are no groceries in the cupboard. Then you come in here empty-handed. What do you think is wrong, Nelson?"

"I don't know, my dear, how we're going to pay the bills around here. There's no money, and that's it," he said.

Jennifer couldn't handle it any longer.

"Who the hell do you think you are? Go in that room, get that money, and go buy some food for me and the girls," she yelled. Her whole body was shaking with rage.

"Oh, you found it, did you," he laughed. "I'll give you some of it."

Nelson went into the room. Jennifer could hear him fumbling with the drawer, then the rattling paper. *Is he really going to give me some of the cash?* Jennifer wondered.

Nelson walked to the table with three $100 bills in his hand. But before Jennifer could take the money, he pulled a lighter out of his pocket.

Nelson set the money on fire, then threw the burning money into the ashtray.

"It's my money, not yours, and not the girls'," he said, and walked away.

There were no words to express her anger, or her fear. Jennifer gathered up the girls and, without supper, got them ready for bed.

The three of them went to bed early that night, but Jennifer didn't feel rested the next morning. Her night was restless. She got up and went through her usual routine of getting the girls ready, but this day would be far from normal.

"I can't take this anymore," Jennifer told Nelson. "Me and the girls are leaving today. I don't have any food, and you're hiding money from us. That's not right. This marriage is over."

"Give me your driver's licence," Nelson demanded. "You won't be driving anywhere this day."

But Jennifer refused, and she realized Nelson was going for her purse, which was sitting on the kitchen chair. She grabbed the purse and put it over her shoulder.

"You're not going anywhere!" he yelled. Nelson grabbed the purse from her shoulder, ripping the strap.

Jennifer ran downstairs, called the police, and waited. Finally, when she saw Nelson leave the apartment, she went back upstairs. By the time the officers arrived, he was long gone. But they had plenty of questions.

"Why didn't you just take the envelope of money?" the officer asked. "You are his wife, and that's your money, too." The RNC officers had looked through the cupboards and understood the dire situation Jennifer faced.

"Mrs. Hart, you have to leave this situation. Pack your bags and some items for the children. We're taking you somewhere safe."

They ended up at a transition house that was being renovated at the time. After a couple of days there, they were moved to a hotel. But it wasn't long before Nelson found out where they were staying and the phone calls began.

"Come back," he pleaded. "I'll give you some of the money, you won't have to worry about groceries anymore. I promise."

"No, Nelson, I have to think about Krista and Karen. You say there will be food, and things will be different, but they never are. I'm not coming back," Jennifer cried into the phone.

But the phone calls persisted. The promises became more persuasive, and Jennifer was finding it harder to say no.

The small hotel room was cramped for the three of them, and Jennifer wanted to go back to her apartment. Her life.

After several more phone calls, Jennifer agreed to go home.

Back at the apartment, she saw that he had stayed true to his word. There were groceries in the cupboards and a new box of diapers for the girls. But there was little to be excited about. In her heart, she knew this wouldn't last for long.

But for now Jennifer felt good to have the girls in their own cribs, and to get the laundry done and packed away in their own little room. The girls seemed more at ease, too.

Nelson was just sitting down to watch television when there was a knock at the door. There stood a man, probably in his mid-forties, carrying a briefcase. Also, a woman who looked no more than twenty-five, and she had a stack of envelopes clutched in her arm.

"Are you Nelson Hart?"

"Yeah, that's me."

"We're with Child, Youth and Family Services. We need to check on the girls to make sure everything is okay. Do you mind if we come in?"

Nelson didn't say a word as the two social workers entered the apartment. He sat at the kitchen table and they followed him. Jennifer sat at the table as well. She was interested in any news that might mean a more stable home for Karen and Krista.

"Jennifer, how are you feeling now that you're back home?" the woman asked. "The staff at the transition house were surprised to learn that you wanted to leave so quickly. We just want to make sure that you are not going back to the same situation. You need food for those girls, and for yourself."

"Them girls will have food, don't you worry about it," said Nelson.

The social worker again addressed Jennifer. "Can we have a look at the food you have here in the house at the moment?"

"Go ahead," said Nelson, "I bought food yesterday before they came home."

The man got up and checked through the cupboards and the fridge. All the while, he was making notes on a clipboard.

"Jennifer, can you tell us, do you have a supply of diapers on hand for the girls right now?" he asked.

Again Nelson replied for her. "She's got plenty of diapers. There's a brand new box in the room."

The social worker stopped and looked directly at Nelson. "I'm going to need more information. Jennifer, can we speak to you in private?"

Nelson sighed and stomped into the living room to express his dissatisfaction with that particular scenario.

Jennifer went into the bedroom with the two social workers.

"Jennifer, we are worried that you are going to end up back in the same situation again. We can't let that happen for the sake of Krista and Karen. We are going to be visiting you from now on. We'll be just checking in to see how things are going. But if we find you in a situation like you were in last week, you will have to leave Nelson. As social workers, we can't let the girls be put at risk. Do you understand?"

"I do," said Jennifer. "You guys are more than welcome to drop by any time. To be honest, it gives me comfort that you are interested in helping me take care of the girls. Whatever I can do to make sure they have a good life, I will do."

"That's good," said the woman, whose name was Deanna. "We're going to leave now, but here's my card. Call me any time, and I'll be here to help as best I can."

Once they had left the apartment, Nelson sat up on the couch.

"You know now that we're being investigated. They'll be watching me all the time," he said. Then he stood up and kicked the coffee table over on its side.

"If you don't stop, I'll be calling the police again," said Jennifer. "What's wrong with having them here? At least they're looking out for Krista and Karen."

But before she could finish her thought, Nelson was out the door.

29

Jennifer watched the familiar sights go by as she and Nelson made their way to Horwood. It was Nelson's hometown, and his brother Mervin still lived there. But Mervin was on the mainland for the time being, and Nelson had just gotten his moose licence. It was the perfect reason for a quick vacation out of the city. And Jennifer was anxious to slow down the pace a little.

Mervin's house was quite a change from their apartment in St. John's, and the girls were loving the extra space and freedom.

As usual, Krista was leading Karen around the house and showing her all the new things they would explore. Karen followed her faithfully and listened carefully to her slightly older sister. In fact, most days she listened to Krista more than her mom. It was good to be in the company of family again.

Nelson's father, who also lived in Horwood, was helping Nelson find his moose. Until one morning, their trip was cut short and the men came home early.

Jennifer didn't know what started the argument between Nelson and his dad, but it quickly grew heated. They were in the basement, and the twins were taking in every word. Back and forth the men argued. When Jennifer tried to stop Nelson's verbal assault on his father, she saw a side of him she didn't know existed.

With Karen and Krista watching, he pushed her chest so hard she fell back onto the floor. The girls started screaming.

His father was quick to react.

"Let that be the last time I ever see you do that to her," his father hissed from between his teeth.

"Come on. We're going back to St. John's right now," said Nelson.

30

By Christmas, things had settled down. Nelson was regularly buying enough food to get by, and there were usually enough diapers in the house. The groceries might not have the best-quality food Jennifer could have asked for, but it was a good Christmas. The girls had plenty of gifts Christmas morning.

When the stores reopened, just after Boxing Day, Nelson suggested they go out for the evening and pick up some extra things they needed for the house. They arranged for the girls to stay downstairs with neighbours, and Jennifer was looking forward to getting out of the apartment.

"Everything you need should be right in this bag," Jennifer told the sitter. "We won't be long."

"The girls will be fine, take your time," she assured Jennifer.

So Jennifer and Nelson headed out to the mall. They took a taxi, and by the time they got there, Nelson was a lot less eager to spend any money, so Jennifer settled for a night of mostly browsing around the mall.

On the taxi ride home, Nelson's mood grew darker. Jennifer wasn't sure what was bothering him, but she certainly didn't feel like asking. For a moment she thought he might be having a seizure and was trying to hide it, like he sometimes did.

But Jennifer was shocked at what happened when the taxi pulled up in front of the apartment building.

Nelson jumped out of the cab and ran into the apartment. Before she realized what was going on, the driver had locked the doors, and she was trapped inside the car. It happened so quickly she thought she was dreaming. What kind of stunt was he pulling this time?

"That's over $15 your husband owes me. You're not getting out of here until he pays up," said the driver.

Jennifer was stunned. She sat in the car, close to tears. She couldn't believe Nelson wasn't coming back for her. Not even to see if she was okay.

After about ten minutes, the driver spoke up.

"You can go in, but if he's not out here in ten minutes, I'm calling the police."

First Jennifer walked into her neighbour's apartment and gathered up Karen and Krista. Feeling numb and confused, she walked up the stairs, and Nelson let her into the apartment.

"Why are the lights off?" she asked.

"I don't want the taxi driver to see us," he said. "I'm not paying him."

"Well, he told me that if you don't go down there and pay him, he's calling the cops," said Jennifer.

"Well, he's about to learn that there's no way I'll be paying that $15. I need that money more than he does."

While Jennifer nervously got the girls ready for bed, Nelson was continuously checking the window. Finally, the police arrived with a loud knock on the door.

Nelson went into the room, and for a minute Jennifer was worried he wouldn't answer. Another rap on the door, and finally Nelson came out of the room with the money in his hand. He opened the door and reluctantly passed them the cash. After a stern warning about the crime he had committed, they left.

31

After Christmas had passed and winter set in, Nelson was spending more and more time around the apartment. Jennifer was glad to see he wasn't gambling, but it wasn't easy having him around all the time.

He didn't have much of a relationship with Karen and Krista, but more often these days they were crying whenever he was around them. In fact, Jennifer was starting to get suspicious he was intentionally making them cry.

She was doing dishes one evening when she heard one of the girls start to cry very suddenly.

"Nelson, what's going on with the girls?" she asked as she walked into the living room.

"I don't know, they're just cranky, I suppose."

"Daddy pinch," said Krista.

The girls were in the playpen, and Nelson was just a couple of feet away on the couch.

Jennifer sized up the situation and went back to the dishes. These days there were a lot of outbursts from the girls while they were in the living room with Nelson. She thought "Daddy pinch" could very well be a possibility.

She grabbed two plates and began hitting them together, as if she were drying them off. Then, slowly, she watched from around the corner at Nelson and the girls, hoping he wouldn't notice her.

For a while the girls were busy jumping up and down. They laughed and bounced, until Nelson reached out with his left hand to pinch Krista first. As soon as she shrieked, he pinched Karen.

Jennifer watched in disbelief.

"You can't do that to those girls," yelled Jennifer as she came out from behind the corner.

Caught in the act. Yet he didn't say a word, while

Jennifer screamed at him. Instead, he grabbed his jacket and left.

32

Life in St. John's wasn't getting any easier for Jennifer. Her family remained in Gander, and the city life definitely wasn't for her.

It was difficult getting around with two energetic two-year-olds, and she no longer felt safe at the apartment.

"I'm moving back to Gander," she announced one day in March. She knew Nelson didn't want to leave St. John's, but she no longer cared. "If you don't want to go, you can stay here. Me and the girls will go back on our own."

Child services required she contact them, so the next morning she was on the phone to let them know. By lunchtime, there was a knock on the door.

"Hi, Jennifer, we'd like to talk for a moment."

She invited the social workers in, but she knew there was no use in them trying to convince her to stay.

The lady who did all the talking was someone Jennifer had never met before, but she seemed friendly enough.

"Jennifer, we are here because we want to make sure you are making the best decision for the girls. Where are you going?" she asked.

"I have to go back to Gander. I don't like the fast pace here in St. John's, and I think Gander would be a safer environment."

"What about food? Has Nelson been giving you money?"

Jennifer responded, "Yes he has. We're fine."

"Well, that's difficult to believe, considering everything we've witnessed over the past few months. We have to look out for those girls. We will be in touch as soon as you are settled into the new apartment back in Gander."

Before the social worker left, she was required to write an explanation of why the girls were being moved.

"To provide a better environment for the kids," was written on the form. A week later, Jennifer had secured another apartment in Gander, and the family was packing up to move once again.

33

Edgewood Apartments weren't as nice as the home Jennifer had gotten used to in St. John's, but she didn't care. Number 204 was home. Gander was home, and she was thankful to have some family around for support. Of course, child services were there right away, and she took comfort in knowing that they'd be making sure they wouldn't have to do without. But life with Nelson wasn't about to get any easier.

He was never at home anymore. Jennifer felt like he was becoming more interested in living a single life without her and the kids. While they had enough food to get by, he controlled the money. And she believed that most of it was going into the slot machines.

Mervin showed up for a visit. After a few games with the girls, he gave Jennifer $50 and told her to go buy some groceries. But upon leaving, he called Jennifer to say that he had spotted Nelson after he left the apartment. Nelson was sitting in his car at the local Kentucky Fried Chicken eating his meal, while her girls had nothing. She knew Mervin had just about had enough.

Then there were the pills. She made sure he was taking his seizure medication, but she noticed how fast the painkillers were disappearing lately. There were no grand mal seizures these days, but Nelson continued having partial seizures. Most of the time, he tried to hide them. Sometimes she'd catch him patting his stomach in the bathroom, and he would deny that he was having a seizure. Jennifer knew differently.

But it was the pain medication that was starting to make Jennifer nervous.

"My stomach is hurting," he announced one afternoon out of the blue. "I'm going over to the hospital. Come with me."

Nelson appeared to be fine, but, as usual, Jennifer agreed. They packed the kids into the car and headed to the emergency. Not once did she hear him complain about his bad stomach along the way, but things changed once they got to the hospital.

"Nelson Hart," came the announcement from the overhead speaker. The family went into Dr. Jenson's office.

Suddenly, Jennifer watched as Nelson's pain became more intense and he pleaded with the doctor for something to help.

"This is a very low dose of morphine," said Dr. Jenson. "I hope this helps, Mr. Hart. Call my office tomorrow if you have any problems."

Jennifer watched as Nelson calmed down.

"I'm sure I got something wrong with me," Nelson said as they drove home. "I got cancer and you fellows are all hiding it."

"Nelson, you don't have cancer, my son," said Jennifer. "The doctors have all looked you over, and you've had plenty of tests done. Stop worrying about it."

Nelson was okay for the next few days, but it wasn't long before he started complaining about a headache.

Jennifer had a good idea that the headache was just another reason to look for more pain medications. Sure enough, in less than a week he was headed back to the hospital. This time, she wasn't interested in going with him.

Instead, she chose to spend some quality time at home with the girls without having to worry about Nelson or his mood swings.

She fixed a nice lunch, and she and the girls watched some television. When Karen and Krista got bored with watching Barney, she pulled out their favourite chair. It was an old office chair, but the girls loved having Mom spin them around until they were dizzy.

They were laughing when the phone rang. It was Dr. Jenson.

"We've got a problem over here," he explained. "Nelson came in here complaining about pain, and we were giving him a small dose of morphine with intravenous. A couple of minutes in, he started asking for you. We told him he would have to wait," he explained. "Jennifer, he ripped out the IV and said he was going home. He yelled at our receptionist and told her he believed he has cancer, and that we're hiding it."

Jennifer sat down. She could feel that there was going to be a lot more to this story.

"That's when he told the receptionist that he was going to go home and blow his brains out. Are you there?"

"I'm listening," she replied.

"We had no choice but to call the police," he explained. "Now we don't know where Nelson is, but the police are on their way to your apartment."

It wasn't long after the police showed up.

"Do you have any firearms in the house?" they asked. "Or do you know of any place he could find a gun tonight? We're taking his threat very seriously."

"The only person I know with a gun would be his mother's boyfriend," Jennifer told them.

The police left shortly after, and the phone rang.

"I don't know why you guys are hiding the fact that I have cancer," said Nelson.

"Where are you, Nelson? The police were just here looking for you." Jennifer couldn't recall ever hearing Nelson sounding so scared.

"I'm not telling you," he said. "I saw the police there, and I'm not coming home. I'm going to St. John's, and I'm going to get the doctors there to tell me the truth about the cancer."

And Nelson stayed true to his word and drove to St. John's.

The next time Jennifer would talk to Nelson, he was in St. John's. He went to the hospital, just as he had said he would. But it didn't take the police long to catch up with him. In the parking lot of the Health Sciences Centre, he was arrested and brought to the Waterford Hospital, where he would receive an evaluation of his mental condition.

Jennifer was concerned, but she was also relieved. Without Nelson around, there was less work and less to worry about. There were no outbursts and no fights that dragged on for hours. After a few days, she started getting used to the peace and quiet.

Until one afternoon, when she heard footsteps in the hallway: pacing back and forth. The footsteps didn't stop, and she became curious. That's when she heard the key in the door and realized Nelson had been released from the hospital and was home.

He walked in without a word to either Jennifer or the girls. There was no excitement in this homecoming. The twins didn't even acknowledge him entering the room. He walked on into the bedroom, where he slept for most of the afternoon.

The fun and laughter of the past few days drifted away. Jennifer waited to see what would happen next.

34

When Nelson woke, Jennifer knew that he was getting ready to go out. She didn't know where he was going, and she didn't care. These days she just assumed he was going to the bar to spend the day in front of the slot machines. She highly doubted he was capable of becoming involved with another woman.

Over the next few days, he was quieter than usual. He was also becoming agitated.

"People knows I was in the Waterford," he said. "I knows they're all talking about me."

Jennifer ignored him, but she could see that he always had something on his mind these days.

But today there was work to be done, and as usual Nelson would be no help. She got the girls ready and headed to the mail. She was looking forward to getting her family allowance. The monthly social assistance cheque was gone, and she needed the money. She found her bank card and called the number on the back to make sure the money was in her account.

Her balance was fifty cents.

"Nelson," she yelled. "I don't know what we're going to do, but for some reason the family allowance cheque isn't in the bank. That should have been there yesterday, and I know everyone else got theirs."

"That's not your money. That's my money to spend however I want," he told her.

"The cheque is in my name," she replied. "That's my money for me and the girls."

"Not anymore," he said.

While Nelson had been in St. John's, he had gone to the bank. Forging Jennifer's signature, he had switched the direct deposit so that the money went to his personal account.

Jennifer had no choice but to go to the welfare office. For the next two days she had to explain her situation time and again to several different people. Finally, they gave her an emergency payment of $75.

35

"They all thinks I'm crazy," Nelson said. "Everyone knows I was in the Waterford, and now they're all looking at me strange."

Jennifer was getting sick of hearing it. Even though he was rarely home, all he ever talked about was the way people were looking at him. That, or he was complaining that he needed more painkillers.

"We need groceries, Nelson. Can you stop talking about this stuff and go to the store for me?"

"You go," he said.

Jennifer was surprised. Nelson always did the shopping. In fact, he hated for her to go anywhere, especially alone.

"Well, I'm not taking the girls out in this rain," she said.

"Leave them here with me," Nelson suggested.

Jennifer could hardly believe what she was hearing. In fact, she figured this was probably the first time in the girls' short lives that he had offered to spend time with them alone. She could only speculate that his suspicions were getting the better of him.

She wasn't a hundred per cent confident in leaving the twins alone with him, but she needed food. And going to the store alone with money in her pockets was a rare occasion.

Although it was a cold rain, she enjoyed the walk to the grocery store. And even though she felt like taking her time to enjoy the excursion, the girls were a constant thought.

By the time she reached the checkout, she was anxious to get home. Fortunately, the rain had stopped by the time she left the store, and she made a brisk walk back to the apartment.

By the time she reached the apartment, she was out of breath, both from nearly jogging home, and her anxiety to make sure everything was okay with the girls.

When the door opened, Krista ran to her, and Jennifer knew right away—something wasn't right. Karen was nowhere to be seen, but the sight in front of Jennifer was unimaginable. The two potties were side by side in the hallway. It looked like one of the girls had taken a poop in her potty. But very little of the feces remained in the little pink pot. It was smeared across the walls. When Karen walked into the hallway, Jennifer realized it was in her hair, her clothes, and she had tracked it through the apartment.

"Nelson," she yelled. "What happened here, my son?"

"I don't know what they were doing," he sang out from the bedroom.

She asked Karen and Krista what had happened. No response.

Jennifer dropped the bags and began the process of cleaning up. First she put Karen into the bathtub and washed her from head to toe. Then she started in on the apartment, cleaning the potties first. But as she began washing the walls, she made a disturbing realization.

In many places, the feces was smeared almost to the height of the pictures on the walls.

One thing she knew for sure. The girls hadn't made this mess without some help from someone a lot taller than they were.

36

Nelson insisted he knew nothing about what had happened to the potties, or how a two-year-old's poop ended up being smeared five feet up the wall. But pursuing it any further wasn't worth it. The mood swings were intense.

"How's your sister Susan getting on at the fish plant in Prince Edward Island?" he asked her one day.

"They're doing all right," said Jennifer, wondering where the conversation was going.

"We should move up there. I wonder if she could get us jobs," he suggested.

Jennifer felt like they had just gotten settled in from their move back from St. John's, but maybe a change would do them good.

After a couple of conversations with her sister, they were pretty much guaranteed work. By April they had packed up their belongings once again and headed to PEI. Nelson wanted to get away from the shame of being in a mental institution, and Jennifer was looking forward to seeing her sister. Also, this was a chance to start making some money instead of living on welfare.

Their apartment was good, and it didn't take Jennifer long to find a sitter for the kids. The wages at the fish plant were good and the work was fairly easy. As the lobsters came down the line, Jennifer and Nelson pulled off the antennae. It seemed easy enough, but after three days Nelson was complaining that he was having pains. By day four, he quit.

And even though Jennifer was willing to continue on, circumstances wouldn't allow it.

Every day she would come home from work to find Karen and Krista were stomach sick. At first she thought it might be just a change in diet, but a visit to the doctor revealed that the girls were having a tough time being separated from their mother for the first time.

That sealed it. They were moving home. This time, instead of packing, Nelson decided the best thing to do was to sell off their furniture to make the return trip a little easier.

37

May 2002.

Moving back to Newfoundland wasn't going to be as easy as their previous moves, Jennifer soon learned.

Social services made it quite clear that they had to be living in the province for at least thirty days before they could qualify for any type of assistance. Everything they owned was in the trunk.

Not knowing where to turn, Jennifer went to the place she knew would never turn her away: the Salvation Army.

"I don't know what to do," she explained to the Captain. "We've spent all our money on the trip here, and we can't move in with Nelson's mother. Can you help us?"

"Of course, we would do anything to ensure those girls aren't on the street," he replied. "We have an arrangement with a motel operator here in town who can let you stay there. We'll give you some food, but that's about all we can promise right now."

The officer went and made a very brief phone call. He turned to Jennifer and said, "One week. The room is only available for seven nights."

It wasn't a permanent solution, but it would help for now. Jennifer and Nelson drove to the motel and brought the girls inside. Nelson walked in, had a brief look around, and was gone. For the next seven nights he slept there, but during the days Jennifer had no idea what he was up to. All the while, she worried about where they would go when they had to leave.

Both Jennifer's parents were willing to have them move in until the month was up, but Nelson wanted no part of it.

"I don't want you and the girls going down there," he said.

Jennifer felt like Nelson didn't want her going anywhere these days. She stayed at the hotel and tried to figure out where they would go.

"Mervin, how are you doing?" Jennifer asked. Nelson's brother had helped her many times, and she hoped he would be there again.

"I'm doing good. More importantly, how are you and the

girls? Mom told me you guys were back from PEI. Is Nelson having any of his moods these days?"

Jennifer replied, "To be honest, we don't see much of him, Mervin, and I can't say I really care. Our problem now is that in a couple of days we aren't going to have anywhere to live, and Nelson don't care one bit."

"I'm sick of the way my brother is treating you and those girls," said Mervin. "I can't say I want him around, but you know you and those girls are always welcome at this house."

Jennifer was relieved. But when she told Nelson, he was mad.

"I don't need his help," yelled Nelson. "What's going on with the two of you, anyway? You know what I thinks? I thinks Mervin wants you. I think he wants you and those girls. Perfect little ready-made family."

When the day came to leave the motel, Nelson managed to put aside his jealousy. The family made the drive to Horwood. Jennifer was happy to be in the company of someone who would look out for her and the kids. But that didn't last long. Nelson quickly started putting pressure on Jennifer to go back to Gander and work on getting social assistance back in place. So she left the girls with Mervin.

But her attempts were futile, and after just a couple of days the family was back in the car. This time they would make the journey to Wesleyville to stay with Jennifer's father.

Again, she was glad to be with someone she loved. Someone who loved and cared for her.

"Jennifer, there's something wrong with Nelson," her father told her. "Sometimes he makes me afraid. Are you sure you're okay?"

"We're fine," she lied. "He's gone most of the time, anyway. Once we get this apartment, everything will be okay." Her dad was always worried about the little things, and Jennifer didn't take his concerns seriously.

For the first two days at her father's, Nelson continued to make himself scarce. The house had three bedrooms and was plenty comfortable for Karen and Krista. But there were few words to describe Jennifer's mental state. Nelson's mood swings were constant, whenever he was around. She was tired. They had been on the move for a month and a half. Bouncing from one province to another. From one town to another. All the while, taking care of two very energetic two-year-olds.

One afternoon, when Jennifer was making tea for her father, Nelson burst through the door.

"I heard you fellows talking about me," he screamed. "I don't have to take this." Jennifer and her father exchanged a knowing glance. They had not been talking about Nelson. In fact, they had been sitting in silence. But that didn't stop the verbal attack Nelson made against her father. He continued his tantrum until he fled out the door.

Jennifer had very little to say about the incident. She knew that her father might very well be right to worry about the situation.

Four hours later, Nelson walked back in as if nothing had happened.

"Do you know where I was?" he announced as he plopped into a chair at the kitchen table. Jennifer's father had already left the house to run some errands.

"I was at the cemetery this whole time. Just sitting there."

Jennifer ignored him and decided to check on the girls.

From behind her he said, "Pack the clothes. The apartment is ready in Gander. Come on, lets go."

Jennifer was excited to hear the apartment was ready, but it was late in the day. Gander was a three-hour drive, and it would be tough on the girls. But she packed their bags, said her goodbyes, and they were off.

38

The drive to Gander was taking forever. Nelson was driving slower than usual, and the sky was starting to darken. Jennifer sat back and chose not to open her mouth. If she did mention it, he'd probably drive even slower.

Finally, when they did get to Gander, Nelson wanted to go shopping.

"I'm not going anywhere, except to the apartment to get the girls straightened away," she argued. The travelling was taking its toll on everyone, and Jennifer just wanted to rest her head in her own apartment before dark.

"I don't think the apartment is ready," said Nelson.

Silence. There was nothing to say. It was too much to even begin to understand.

"You're telling me that we drove in here tonight and we don't have anywhere to stay?" Jennifer yelled. The girls started to cry, seeing their mother so upset. Jennifer put her thoughts together once more.

"Call your mother," she said.

"No. She don't want to see me, and I don't want to see her," said Nelson. "We're going to sleep in the car."

"Oh my God!" Jennifer cried. "What the hell are we going to do? Those girls are not going to be sleeping in this car!"

After a few moments, Jennifer asked Nelson to drive her to the mall. She got out of the car, went inside, and found a pay phone.

"You have to help me," Jennifer told Tammy, her social worker, over the phone. "He's brought me to Gander, and he expects us to sleep in the car."

"Meet me at the airport in ten minutes."

Jennifer climbed back into the car with Nelson and told him to drive to the airport.

Tammy told her she would meet her there, along with an RCMP officer.

When Nelson stopped, Jennifer got out and walked over to Tammy's car. The police officer asked Jennifer to sit inside so they could talk.

"What are your options?" Tammy asked her.

"Well, I don't really have any, that's why I called you. Can you get us an apartment, and some money?" Jennifer asked.

"Like we said, you're going to have to wait. Right now our concern is with you and the girls—not Nelson. Who can we call? Is there anyone in your family?"

"I guess you could call Nelson's brother Mervin," she said.

Tammy began pushing the buttons as Jennifer read the phone number from her address book. She could hear her brother-in-law as he picked up the phone, and she listened as Tammy asked him whether he could help.

Tammy hung up. "Mervin has agreed to take you and the girls, but he doesn't want his brother."

Jennifer wasn't surprised. "Nelson won't be happy about this."

"Let's talk to Nelson," said the RCMP officer as he opened the door.

"Look, Mr. Hart, we have a bit of a situation here," he stated, as Nelson stared into his lap. "You don't have any money to feed your family. You don't even have a roof to put over their heads tonight. Your brother doesn't want you in his house, but he is willing to take care of your family. My suggestion is that you give them a ride to Mervin's house, where they'll be comfortable and safe."

Jennifer could see the anger in Nelson's eyes. Suddenly, he pulled a wallet from his pocket. To Jennifer's amazement he brought forward a Capital One credit card.

"I've got money to put them in a hotel tonight. They ain't going with Mervin this night."

The social worker gave Jennifer her contact information, and then drove away.

At least she and the girls would have a pillow for tonight.

Tomorrow they would make the three-hour drive back to Wesleyville—back to Jennifer's father—to wait.

39

June 2002.

The move to Edgewood Apartments number 311 would be one of the easiest Jennifer had ever made.

There was no furniture. Nelson had sold everything before they came home from Prince Edward Island. Everything they owned was in the car: a few bags of clothes and the girls' stroller.

Jennifer carried the bags upstairs, and Nelson was soon off in the car, leaving them on their own. Perhaps he was at the bar. Maybe he was somewhere else. Jennifer was too tired to care.

The only unpacking she had to do was the few necessities belonging to the girls. Thankfully, Nelson hadn't sold all the toys while they were in PEI, so there were a few things to keep them occupied in the bare apartment. There was no television, no dishes. Not even curtains for the windows. But there was no point in worrying about that now. Jennifer was thankful it was the peak season for yard sales. Over the next few weeks she would try and find a few deals on furniture and turn the empty apartment into a home.

She was also grateful that they had taken some blankets and pillows with them as well.

That night she used all the blankets she owned to make a bed for the girls on the floor.

She slept beside them on the carpet, with no blanket and a pillow made of a stack of her own clothes.

But despite the hardship, there was a bright spot in the

situation. Someone at social services had taken the initiative to take the welfare cheque out of Nelson's name and put it in Jennifer's. That was perhaps the only reason she had cupboards that were full of food.

After a few days in the apartment, Jennifer had also managed to track down a couch that doubled as a sofa bed. Nelson agreed to stay with the girls while Jennifer and her neighbour drove down to pick up the couch. Jennifer and her neighbour moved the couch up the stairs and into the apartment. All the while, Nelson was in the bathroom.

The workers with child services began visiting as soon as she was in the apartment. For Jennifer, their visits brought comfort and security. The first worker Jennifer had gotten close to was Tammy.

"How are you feeling with all the moving around?" Tammy asked her as she looked around the empty apartment.

"Not bad, a little tired, but I'm okay."

"What about the girls?" Tammy asked.

"They are okay, but it's busy managing everything," Jennifer said.

"Well, we're looking into ways that we might be able to get you some extra help with the girls," said Tammy. "But right now you have to concentrate on getting settled into this apartment and making sure the girls' needs are met."

But the one thing Jennifer neglected to tell the social worker was exactly how tough it was living with Nelson. Though he was never home, there was always anxiety each morning she put her feet on the floor. She wondered what each day would bring.

There was the gambling and his absence from their lives. But worst of all were the mood swings. Jennifer had managed to bring a clock when she returned from PEI. It was one that she had taken a particular liking to and didn't want to leave behind. She hung it in the kitchen in a prominent space. It was elegant, unlike her current surroundings. One day, shortly after they'd moved in, came a rare afternoon when Nelson was at home. But, more like him, he was in the bedroom napping while Jennifer sat with the girls in the living room.

But from the living room she had a clear view of Nelson as he walked out of the bedroom, only half awake, and grabbed the clock from the wall. He raised it above his head, and in disbelief Jennifer watched as he smashed it onto the floor. He then turned around and went back to bed.

Jennifer screamed at him for answers, but like many other occasions, he ignored her tantrums and pretended like nothing had happened.

Then there were the times when he was the one who did the screaming. Those were harder.

"Why don't you have supper ready?" he would yell.

And while Jennifer would answer, it fell on deaf ears. He would follow her around the apartment, screaming. During those tirades, he would lose track of the reason he was mad and just keep going. In their few weeks at Edgewood, their landlord and neighbours got to know them well. In the middle of one of his moods, the landlord showed up at the door to tell them to keep the noise down.

40

July 2002.

Jennifer had kept herself busy over the past month. After finding the couch, she kept going to yard sales until she'd also managed to find a dining table and a box spring and mattress. When Nelson suggested a road trip out of town, she didn't hesitate. She was looking forward to getting away from the apartment. Everywhere she looked there were things she needed. There weren't even any curtains. So she had taken an old bedsheet, cut it in two, and hung the two halves in the living room window. In a sad sort of way, she was happy they had no friends. At least there was no one to see how bad things really were.

So they decided to go see Jennifer's mother on the south coast of the island. It was a couple of hours drive, but they were all excited to get going. The weather was perfect for a road trip.

"Teddy bear song, Mommy," Krista called out from the back seat.

"Again?" Jennifer laughed. "You girls are going to wear out that tape."

The song was one for which the girls had developed a fondness, perhaps just because it was about a teddy bear, but Jennifer loved watching their reactions when they heard it. She played it over and over for them. Each time, they enjoyed it as much as the last.

Jennifer rewound the tape to the right spot and, as predicted, the girls lit up when the song started. But their joy didn't last too long.

Nelson pressed the eject button. He took the tape and flung it out the window without a word or any sort of explanation.

"Oh no," Jennifer cried. Then the cries began in the back seat when the music came to a halt.

"What did you have to go and do that for?" she snapped.

He continued to ignore her. Finally, she gave up, and they continued to drive in silence.

He was the first to speak, and Jennifer will never forget the words.

"I hates Krista," he said. "I hates those youngsters."

"What the frig did those kids ever do to you for you to say that?" Jennifer said.

There was no response, and Jennifer put it behind her for the rest of the trip.

41

"Get the girls ready, Jennifer," announced Nelson.

"Where are we going?" she asked. "My son, there's too much work to be done here this evening for me to be going out for a drive."

"Well, you don't have to go," he said. "I want to take the girls to the playground."

Jennifer wasn't quite sure how to react. There'd only been one other occasion where Nelson had taken the girls to the playground, and she wasn't sure she fully trusted him to take care of them. She wasn't even sure he could strap them into their seats properly. But she was happy that he was at least making an effort. These days she believed the only thing that mattered to him was being in front of the slot machines at the bar or causing arguments at home. She'd had very little peace since they had moved home from PEI.

But instead of arguing, she decided maybe a day with their dad would do the girls good. The weather was hot. There was laundry and dishes to be done.

"All right, but don't be gone long," she said.

Jennifer got the girls dressed in their matching summer outfits, perfect for a July afternoon at the playground. She packed everything, from snacks to Band-Aids, and sent the three of them on their way.

As Jennifer cleaned the house, the girls were on her mind.

She was nervous. What if Nelson wasn't watching them? she worried. But she forced it to the back of her mind. On a positive note, if something did go wrong, at least Krista was now old enough to tell her what had happened.

Nearly two hours later, Nelson returned home with the girls.

"Ice cream!" Krista was bubbling with excitement.

"Ice cream?" questioned Jennifer as she looked at Nelson.

"We went to Lewisporte," he said. "I bought them ice cream while we were out there."

"Why would you drive half an hour away for ice cream?" asked Jennifer. "I thought you were going to the playground up the street."

"I don't know," he said. "It just seemed like a good idea for a drive."

42

July 29, 2002.

"Good morning, Jennifer," Tammy said as Jennifer opened the apartment door.

The girls were giggling and playing with their dolls in the living room while Nelson was making tea in the kitchen. It seemed like the workers from child welfare were visiting at least a couple of times a week, and Jennifer knew that it was making Nelson furious. He was beyond embarrassed.

"I know we've been here a lot," she said. "But we have to make sure that you and the girls aren't doing without.

"I don't mind," said Jennifer. "I'm just glad to know you guys are watching out for me."

And these days Jennifer was in need of more support, as they suspected. Nelson had gone to social services with a request to have the cheques sent to him. So, for the past month, he was back in control of the money, and things were getting tough.

"Jennifer, you realize the girls will soon be starting school," said Tammy. "We're suggesting it would be good for them to be in a social environment on a part-time basis. That would give you a break for three days a week, and we think it would be good for Krista and Karen to make some friends."

From the sudden burst of dishes hitting the bottom of the sink, there was no mistaking how Nelson felt about the idea. For the next few minutes, Jennifer and Tammy could barely carry on their conversation over the sounds of smashing dishes and Nelson's mumbling.

Finally, Tammy gave up. "Jennifer, I want you to think about this. I will have a look at some possible arrangements and I'll let you know what we come up with. I'll be back in a couple of days."

Once the door closed, and Tammy was out of the building, Nelson turned to Jennifer.

"They aren't going to no daycare," said Nelson.

"But you heard what Tammy said. They need to get used to other kids, and I need a break every now and again," she said.

"Well, you can put it out of your mind. I'm not having the youngsters going to no daycare."

43

August 3, 2002.

It was a beautiful day, and Jennifer had spent the day in the apartment with the girls. The days were quiet, but busy. Jennifer was finally turning the apartment into a home, but it was taking some work with two active little girls scrambling around. She still felt tired from the moving around and the stress of the past spring. She just needed to get out.

"Nelson, let's take the girls out this evening," she suggested. "I need to get out of this apartment or I'm going to go crazy. Why don't we take the girls to the playground after supper?"

When he started to walk away, Jennifer was worried he'd be leaving again before she could even get an answer. Finally, he agreed.

"Let's go out to Cobb's Pond," she suggested.

The pond was only a couple of kilometres away from the apartment, and there was plenty to keep the girls busy. Not only was there a big area for them to run and burn off some energy, but there was also a set of swings and a see-saw. For Karen and Krista, it was the perfect place. They were bubbly little girls who loved to giggle, skip, and run. But their favourite activity was always using the swings, especially when they could convince Mommy to get on with them.

Tonight was no different. Jennifer struggled to keep up with them as they ran around the park, laughing and full of life.

Nelson stayed in the car and watched them for over an hour.

Finally, Jennifer and the girls headed back to the car. It felt so good to be outside, and the girls needed the freedom. Jennifer wasn't ready to go back to the apartment. Once the girls were strapped into their seats, Jennifer had an idea. "Why don't we take a ride out to Little Harbour? I heard they have new swings there now."

It was about a ten-minute drive out the highway, and then down a small gravel road. The last stretch of road dropped off sharply down to Gander Lake, in an area known as Little Harbour.

From the top of the hill, Jennifer could see the wharf, where a few people were still swimming after the heat of the day. Others were still out on the lake or bringing their boats in for the night. The isolated area of Gander Lake looked beautiful this time of the evening. The dark water reflected the surrounding hills perfectly in the calm.

It didn't take long before the girls eyed what they were looking for: the swings. They started to shriek with excitement.

Nelson parked by the water, and the girls weren't long

springing into action once Jennifer let them out of their car seats. The three of them went directly to the swings.

Jennifer jumped into the swing herself. Then Krista climbed up onto one leg while Karen jumped onto the other. They both hung onto their mom's neck, as Jennifer started to swing higher, and higher. The higher and faster she would go, the more the girls laughed.

"Higher, Mommy!"

Despite the enormous amount of fun they were having, Nelson stayed on the beach by the wharf. He didn't swim. In fact, he was afraid of the water more than anything. But he sat on the shore the whole time, completely unaware of his family. Instead, he watched the swimmers as, one by one, they continued jumping off the end of the wharf, until the sun nearly set.

By the end of the evening there were only a couple of people left at Little Harbour. As night closed in quickly, Jennifer put the girls' safely back in the car, and they drove home to Gander.

44

August 4, 2002.

"The girls are sleeping," Jennifer informed Nelson when he woke up. "Try not to wake them. I think they're worn out from last night."

They hadn't gotten home until after nine o'clock. Jennifer had put them into the tub and got them off to bed as early as possible. Today was going to be a big day.

Every year the town of Gander holds a demolition derby, which brings out nearly everyone in town. This year the town had installed new stands, so Jennifer figured the girls were old enough to take in the event from the seats.

When they finally woke, Jennifer got them breakfast. As soon as they had finished eating, they started giggling and ran straight for the living room. They were getting ready for playtime, but in order to have them both ready for the derby in time, Jennifer started getting them ready right away.

"All right, girls," she called out. "We're going to put your hair up into ponytails today."

It was rare for the girls to wear their hair up, but Jennifer thought it would like nice for the big day out. Then it was Jennifer's turn to get ready. But before she got into the bath, the girls started acting up. "Mommy, Karen's pulling my hair," said Krista.

"Come on, now, girls, Mommy has to get ready," said Jennifer. When she looked, she noticed their hair was already getting messed up. They were bored and restless.

"I can take them to the playground so you can get ready," said Nelson.

"Okay," said Jennifer. "Just give me a minute to get their travel bag ready."

Inside, Jennifer packed snacks, extra clothes, and sunscreen. By the time she was finished, the girls had everything they needed for the day. Even though they wouldn't be gone long, it was a standard practice to make sure they had all the necessities whenever they went out.

All dressed and ready to go, she walked her beautiful little daughters to the door.

And in a moment Jennifer would never forget, they both looked at her. Simultaneously they both said, "Mommy, we come back for you, okay?"

She waved them off and went to run the bath. She assumed Nelson was going to the playground down the street and would be back in less than an hour. She didn't want to keep the girls waiting when they got back.

It wasn't often Jennifer was home alone, so she enjoyed the warmth and comfort of the bath on this particular morning. Last night had left her feeling rejuvenated, and she was looking forward to the derby.

But the day was waiting, so she got out and started getting dressed. After her clothes were on, she put on her makeup as she usually did.

Her hair was still wrapped in a towel when her life changed forever.

"Jennifer, Jennifer!" Nelson was yelling. He was out of breath from running. He burst into the apartment. "Krista is in the water, and I can't find Karen."

"What are you talking about?" She knew from the panic in his eyes that something was seriously wrong.

"The girls are at the lake!" He tried to catch his breath.

Time stood still as Jennifer ran down the stairs of the building. The towel from her hair landed next to the apartment door as she fled. The police would find it there in the same location several hours later.

"I just remembered, Karen is in the car," he said as they ran to the car.

She looked in the car. No Karen.

"Karen's not here," she cried, looking around the parking lot. "Where is she?"

"I left her down there," he said.

"Where?"

"Little Harbour."

"Let's go," she cried. She got in the car, confused. Where were the girls? Why wasn't Nelson giving her a straight answer about what had happened?

From then on, time began to slow down.

"Drive faster," she yelled as she and Nelson made their way down the highway in his Dodge Shadow.

"My foot is to the floor," he said.

But that wasn't how it felt to Jennifer. For the next ten minutes, Jennifer felt like the car was barely moving. She couldn't tell if Nelson was lying to her about how fast he was going or whether time was standing still.

Either way, she couldn't get to Little Harbour fast enough.

The familiar landmarks moved past the window of the car in what seemed to be slow motion to Jennifer. The Irving truck stop, the radio station. In what felt like an eternity, they passed an area known as Tower Hill. Nelson sat behind the wheel quietly.

Finally, they made the left turn off the Trans-Canada Highway and went down the dirt road that would take them to Little Harbour.

The car finally topped the last hill looking down toward the vast, dark lake. It had never looked so ominous. It was isolated, and today the place that had been so joyous last night was terrifying. It was an overcast morning. Calm. There was no one around, of course. Everyone would be getting ready for the derby by now.

Jennifer's eyes scanned the landscape before her. There was an eerie darkness in the surrounding hills and the glass-like reflection of Gander Lake. Prominent in the horseshoe-shaped inlet, there was a rickety old wharf slightly to the left. It was the same one where Nelson had sat last night, watching the teenagers as they swam and jumped from the end of the wharf.

And although they were still quite a distance away, Jennifer's eyes were drawn to the floating piece of cloth next to the wharf. The cloth, she knew, was the little T-shirt she had put on Krista not long ago.

"Go get help," she said, as the car came to a stop and she got out. She stumbled, not realizing the car was still moving, as she headed toward the wharf. She turned around to realize Nelson was still there. "Get help!" she screamed.

"Krista, Krista! Can you hear me?" Jennifer yelled.

She walked out to the end of the wharf. She moved carefully, knowing she couldn't swim and there was no one here to help her.

She's still alive, I've got to help her, she thought. But Krista was too far away for Jennifer to reach. Shaking, crying, and yelling for Karen, she went to the trees nearby.

"Karen! Where are you? It's Mommy, please come out!" Jennifer felt numb. She could hardly believe what was happening as she went into the woods trying to find a stick.

She fell, and got up. She grabbed every stick in sight, but none of them was long enough for the job she needed to do.

Finally, she found a long branch and ran back to the wharf.

There was no movement from Krista. She was face down, and there was no response. But in Jennifer's mind there was hope. If only she could get her out of the water.

"Krista! Krista!"

Using the stick, she lay down on the wharf and reached to try and hook Krista's clothes. But there was no way. The closest she could get was just a couple of feet away.

And where was Nelson? Again she wondered if time had stopped, but it seemed like Nelson was taking too long.

"Karen," she continued to call out. Suddenly, she had an image of Karen being caught in the woods, trapped and hurt. She ran back to the forest and started tearing her way through the brush. She swatted away the stinging branches, expecting at any minute to see her little girl. But there were no replies to her calls.

She felt like she had been searching for hours.

At last, Jennifer sat, in the extreme silence of the lake, and cried until she heard the approaching sirens. It seemed like it had taken hours for help to arrive. For her there was still hope—they would rescue Krista, and then she could go back to searching for Karen.

They were her family. They were her everything, and without them Jennifer knew her world would collapse.

45

"You have to come with us now, Jennifer," said the paramedic as he put his arm around her.

"I'm not leaving here without Karen," she cried.

"I'm really sorry, Jennifer, but we need you at the hospital with Krista. The police will be here to search for Karen, and they'll let you know as soon as they find anything."

When the paramedics arrived, Jennifer stood in shock. She watched as one of them walked out into the water and picked up Krista's little body. The little girl who was so full of life lay limp in his arms. Jennifer wondered whether Krista's body must have floated closer to the shore while she was searching for Karen in the trees.

Now she stood at the back of the ambulance and looked inside. The attendants began moving mechanically, hooking up wires to the little three-year-old body that lay on the stretcher.

"I can't leave," said Jennifer. "I don't know what to do."

"You have to go with Krista," said the paramedic.

Reluctantly, Jennifer climbed into the back of the ambulance. She noticed Nelson had already started the car and was driving back toward the hospital to meet them.

As she sat beside Krista, she could swear there were little movements in her body. Little signs of encouragement. Jennifer refused to believe this could be the end of such a short life. The attendants had asked her not to try and touch her daughter because of the web of wires and tubes. For Jennifer, Krista looked so fragile, she wouldn't dare touch her for fear something would go wrong.

46

The trip back to the hospital was mostly a blur of busy ambulance attendants fluttering over Krista.

The only thing Jennifer could remember was the hope she was in a dream.

When they finally arrived back at the hospital, Nelson was already inside. The attendants took Krista into a separate room, and the doctors brought both Nelson and Jennifer into a family room.

From what seemed to be miles away she heard a voice say, "We're just going to have to wait and see."

The ambulance attendants had been giving Krista oxygen using an oxygen bag and by doing cardio compressions. But by the time she was admitted to the hospital, there were no vital signs. Dr. Glenn Loy Son wasn't giving up that easily. They began full cardio pulmonary resuscitation. They put tubes into her lungs to help her breathe and started cardiac compressions. They started an IV and put medications into her lungs to try and restart her heart.

Krista was cold and they tried warming her up. After about an hour and fifteen minutes, they finally got a heart rate. Exactly 12:22 p.m.

But there was still no pulse. Dr. Loy Son continued with cardiac compressions until, six minutes later, there was a pulse.

The tests began on the function of her lungs and kidneys, and it looked like they were working reasonably well.

But Krista had suffered severe brain damage.

What Jennifer didn't know was Karen's body had been recovered on the opposite side of the cove and was brought in about forty-five minutes after her sister.

Karen was pronounced dead as soon as she arrived.

47

Constable Terry Trainor (later corporal) was with the RCMP Major Crime Unit in Gander, on the morning of August 4, 2002.

Once he was provided with the details of what had happened, he quickly headed to the hospital.

He and another officer first went to see Karen's body, where they took photographs. Constable Trainor then gave directions to ensure that neither Nelson or Jennifer could have access to either of the children unless they were accompanied by a police officer.

At that point the constable was near the family room where Nelson and Jennifer were meeting with members of the Salvation Army.

Constable Trainor watched as Nelson came out of the family room with a nurse. He suddenly started looking underneath a stretcher, then opened a cabinet.

That's when the nurse called for security, and Nelson said, "I'm just having a spell, I'm just having a spell." He went back into the family room, but someone from security was assigned to keep an eye on the room.

"We are transferring Krista to the Janeway Children's Hospital in St. John's," Dr. Loy Son told Jennifer. She struggled to keep it together as Constable Trainor walked into the room. The police wanted to speak to both her and Nelson that afternoon, while Krista was being moved to St. John's.

"What about Karen?" she cried. "I need to go back up and look for her."

The police hadn't yet told her that Karen was dead. "We're doing everything we can."

Jennifer stayed at the hospital, but at around four o'clock she and Nelson were taken to the police station in separate police cruisers. At the station, Jennifer felt sick while she tried to go over the details with Constable Letang. They sat in the detachment's coffee room, where Jennifer was asked a series of questions. Nelson was questioned for several hours, until eventually he went back to the lake with the RCMP to explain his version of events.

The police urged Jennifer to stay at the station and get some rest, but she only wanted to go home.

She had no idea how she got back to the apartment, but

Nelson was already there when the officer escorted her in. So was her father, her sister, and brother-in-law.

She was exhausted from crying, and from trying to recall the events of the day.

Nelson's story of the day's events hadn't crossed her mind. It was all too much to bear.

Sleep wouldn't come to her that night. She could barely believe what had happened, and she couldn't distinguish what was real anymore. Each time she closed her eyes, she relived the worst moments of her life. The T-shirt floating on the water, and Krista's little body as it twitched in the ambulance. Then the phone rang in the middle of the night.

"Jennifer, you need to come to St. John's right away," said the doctor. "It's Krista. This can't wait."

48

It was 5:00 a.m. and Jennifer was in the car with her sister Penny, and they were on their way to St. John's.

"Dad is going with Nelson," said Penny from a distant place.

Jennifer could remember only pieces of the trip. Every now and again, there were lights from a community. At other times, she remembers watching her sister drive in silence.

But mostly it was as if her world had collapsed. Nothing was right. Nothing was as it should be.

Then, suddenly, by some means she couldn't recall, she was in the hospital. There was family all around. Nelson, Dad, her sister, cousins, and clergy. They were all there trying to support her.

A nurse brought her into a room. There Krista's little body lay on a table, being kept physically alive by life-support, but she was brain-dead.

"Jennifer, Krista is not going to make it. We have to take

her off life-support, but we wanted to give you some time to say goodbye. But first we are going to go downstairs."

She heard the words, but she had no idea who was speaking. It could have been her family or the doctor. She couldn't take her eyes from Krista, and she couldn't believe life had led her to this moment.

She could feel someone's arms holding her up, as the world went from brightness to darkness.

This isn't real, she told herself. "Someone save my baby!" she yelled at the top of her lungs.

Suddenly, all she wanted to do was see Karen. She tried to push away from the people holding on to her. She didn't realize they were trying to help her, not hold her back.

"I'm going down to see my daughter. If anyone tries to stop me, I'll limb this hospital today," Jennifer shrieked.

Downstairs, Karen's cold, lifeless body lay on a table. Through the tears and anger, Jennifer began examining the little body from head to toe.

"Why is her vagina red?" she cried. "Did someone touch her!" she screamed louder still.

"No, Jennifer, that was because of the drowning," a police officer said to her.

Feeling somewhat reassured, Jennifer wanted to pick up her little girl one last time.

She felt the pain pass through her entire body as she felt the coldness of her once bubbly little three-year-old. How was this possible?

Drenched in tears, she lifted Karen to hold her little head against her shoulder. She remembered the warmth and love when she held her daughters like this only a couple of days ago. Why was this being taken from her? She wanted to die.

"Perhaps Nelson would like to hold her, too?" she heard someone say.

She looked at Nelson's emotionless face through her own tears and passed Karen to him.

He picked up Karen, looked down at her, and immediately passed her back to Jennifer. He left the room to watch from outside. This had to be a dream.

Then Jennifer could feel herself being lowered into a chair. She was in a different room. Krista was in the arms of a nurse, or doctor—Jennifer wasn't sure. But Krista was placed in her arms, and at that moment she could focus on nothing but the little body. Her physical warmth was more comforting than when she held Karen, yet there was the same emptiness. The laughing, fun-loving little soul wasn't there anymore. The ventilator was turned off.

Jennifer straightened out Krista's hair, wishing she could sit her down and put curls in it. She wanted to get her a different outfit. Not this sterile hospital gown.

As she stroked Krista's hair, she sang a hymn. One she had sung to both girls many times in their short lives. She struggled through the tears and the agony to make sure she didn't mess up the words. That's when she realized, Krista, too, would soon be cold.

"No. No! You can't. This is a hospital! You can fix her! Save my baby, please!"

Jennifer had never cried so many tears at once. But as the tears started to slow, she realized that Krista had already died in her arms.

Her family gathered around Jennifer as Krista was taken to the morgue to be with her sister. Jennifer could see the agony in her father's face. But there was nothing anyone could do.

Her girls were gone. Krista's heart had stopped.

Throughout the ordeal, Nelson stayed outside the room and quietly watched through the glass.

49

The drive from St. John's back to Gander had never seemed so long. Penny was behind the wheel. Jennifer's father, Cyril, had reluctantly agreed to drive with Nelson, although he made it clear he didn't feel safe.

As they passed the gas station just on the outskirts of the city, Jennifer felt like they should have already been halfway there. Then there were the pieces of conversation with her sister. There were stretches of silence where she couldn't stop seeing her girls in her mind. She felt empty. Then, when she felt as though they were almost home, she'd see another landmark indicating they'd only driven a few kilometres. It was agony.

Time had stopped, and she had nothing. Her world was taken from her, and this drive was giving her plenty of time to think about it.

"Hello," she heard Penny answering her phone. "Yes, Mervin."

Penny passed the phone to Jennifer.

"Yeah," she managed to say.

"Mom wanted me to call you," said Mervin. "She wanted me to ask you what you are planning to put on the girls for their funeral. She wants to know if you've got their outfits picked out."

Jennifer hung up.

To say she wasn't ready to talk about the funeral was an understatement.

Time stood still for the rest of the agonizing trip. The next thing she knew, she was back in the apartment. She was just waking up, even though she couldn't remember having gone to sleep. How long had she been asleep? Why did she still feel so tired? Where were the girls? The girls. It hit her like a punch in the stomach, and she lost them all over again. The past few days came rushing in. She began to cry uncontrollably.

Penny and Susan came into the room and rushed to her side. But there was nothing they could do for her.

After she had calmed down, they convinced her to

come out into the kitchen so they could talk. But there was nothing Jennifer wanted to hear. Nothing she wanted, only her daughters. The tears started to flow again.

It was Nelson who suggested she take something to relax. The doctor had prescribed something to help her calm down. As soon as Nelson saw her becoming upset, he was there to give her the medication. She slept again.

"You gave them to the police!" She could remember the yelling. It was Nelson. Again, his voice was coming from a place that seemed far away.

"Why did you take my boots?" he was saying to Jennifer's brother-in-law.

"We have the same boots," Winston said. "It was an honest mistake, Nelson. Now calm down."

But as she became more focused, Jennifer understood that Nelson thought Winston had brought his boots to the police, and he was furious.

More sleep.

"This is important," Penny was saying to her. They were standing in the girls' room.

On the bed there were several little matching outfits. A sight that brought Jennifer to her knees.

"The green dresses," she told her sister. "That's what I want them to wear. They're also going to need shoes."

"They don't put shoes on the body," said Penny. "You don't need to worry about that."

"My girls are wearing shoes," she insisted. "Now take me over to the mall so I can buy them some."

Jennifer looked through nearly every pair of shoes in the store. She couldn't decide. Finally, she settled on a pair of Winnie the Pooh sandals for each of them.

Then came the time to decide upon caskets. They had to be white. There was a white one available in Gander, but only one. That wasn't going to be good enough. Jennifer had the funeral home track down a matching casket nearly 400 kilometres away. At least the girls would have the caskets she wanted for them.

That night she was both mentally and physically exhausted, but there would be no sleep. Her sisters wanted her to talk, but that was the last thing she wanted. She no longer felt anything. Life, and the people in it, were becoming just one big blur. Nothing had any meaning.

As she lay in the bed, she didn't care about the conversations going on around her. She ignored most of it. But it was the rattling of bags that made her anxious this night and forced her to return to reality.

"What are you doing?" she asked Nelson and her sister. She was standing in the door to the girls' room, and she could see the drawers had been opened.

"Nelson thought it was best to get rid of the girls' things so it didn't upset you," her sister said.

Jennifer was enraged. It was all she had left. Every little sock meant the world to her. They had no right to touch Krista's and Karen's clothes. How dare they! The two of them were in the bedroom, piling all the girls' belongings into garbage bags.

Jennifer shook with rage. "You've got five minutes to get every last piece of their stuff back where it belongs."

50

Jennifer once more emerged from darkness. She was unsure whether or not she'd had a long sleep, or whether she'd been awake all night.

She was aware of the morning sun and that the apartment was full of life. But that wasn't out of the ordinary these days. It seemed like there was always someone there.

She staggered to the kitchen to see the family having breakfast. Someone was in the shower. Her father guided her to the table, although they all had a good idea she would not be convinced to eat again this morning.

"I've got your clothes ready, Jennifer," said Susan. "After you get some food in your stomach, we'll go and get dressed."

Jennifer looked at the plate in front of her. The last thing she wanted was food, while her little girls had nothing. They were lying alone in caskets at the funeral home. How could she eat?

Then she realized why everyone was so busy. This morning would be their first visit to the funeral home.

This would be her last chance to be a mother to her girls.

With a little help from her sister, she showered, did her hair, and got dressed.

She walked downstairs with her family and got into the car. For the past three years she didn't know what it was like to get into the car without first strapping the girls into their seats. It was another reminder. There were so many reminders these days.

She turned to look at the empty car seats, but they weren't there.

Jennifer wanted to ask Nelson what happened to the car seats, but there were more important things to think about this morning. Her girls were her first priority.

The funeral home was a maze of people, and tears. Every face she looked at was full of sorrow. They said things that all sounded the same. But through it all she kept a close eye on Karen and Krista. She made sure their outfits were perfect.

She eyed the people who continuously touched her daughters. And at the end of the visitation, she could see that their hair had been ruffled by the mourners who touched and kissed them. She didn't like it.

Tomorrow she would fix this.

When she came to the funeral home the next morning, she brought a curling iron and a comb. Again she went through the motions of hugging people, listening to their words, and trying to be strong. But her reality was lying in the caskets. They were all that mattered.

"It's time to go," her sister told her at the end of that second evening.

But as soon as the last person had left, Jennifer walked straight over to an electrical outlet and plugged in the curling iron. Her sister was confused, but she could see Jennifer was determined.

She curled their hair and made sure every strand was in place. She fixed their clothes and looked them over until she was totally satisfied they were perfect.

"Okay, I'm ready to go."

As she left the funeral home, she could hear the conversations of her family members in the lobby. She knew they were waiting for her, but she had very little interest in any of them.

Dad was asking Penny where the sympathy cards were. There were hundreds of cards, from all across the province, stacked in a pile near the door.

The people of Newfoundland are known for reaching out to others in times of need, and this situation was no different. The cards, prayers, and financial donations were coming in constantly. Though Jennifer had few memories of this dark day, she recalled a woman who was visiting from the mainland.

"I was driving to St. John's when I heard your story," she said. "I couldn't drive by without giving you a hug. My heart led me here."

It was another of many cards that contained money, but meeting the stranger had touched Jennifer deeply.

But tonight Jennifer knew that her father was talking about the cards. He wanted to know where they had gone.

Jennifer didn't care about the cards or the money. Back at the apartment, she took another of those little white pills, and darkness came quickly.

She would need her rest to be ready for the funeral.

As soon as she drifted off, she could hear her sister say, "Come on, Jennifer, lets get you ready." It seemed like Jennifer had just sat on the bed, and yet somehow it was already morning. The next thing she knew she was sitting in church, looking around, unsure why she was even here. She had a good idea that the lapses were probably because of the pills, but they were helping to numb the pain.

Suddenly, before her, the two white caskets lay over the girls' graves. They were at the cemetery. Everything came rushing in. Little Harbour. Krista's body as it was taken from her arms. The little white pills, the missing car seats. No, this was no dream.

"I want my youngsters back," she burst out during the prayer. "Stop this, I want them back!"

It took the strong arms of a young family member to hold her, and lead Jennifer away from the cemetery, before she collapsed.

51

For the next few days, Jennifer's life slowly started to resume. She was back to doing the housework. She was picking up the pieces and trying to understand everything that had happened.

The first of her chores was to make sure everything that belonged to Karen and Krista was kept safe. She still didn't know what happened to their car seats.

There were so many unanswered questions.

And talking to Nelson was out of the question these days. He seemed to be having one temper tantrum after another, but there were things she wanted to know.

"Nelson, what happened to the cards that people left for us at the funeral home?" she asked.

"They're out in the car," he said.

"What about the money? How much is there? We have bills to pay for the funeral, and I need money for the laundry."

"I already spent the money," he told her. "You'll have to wait for the cheque to get groceries."

Jennifer didn't have the energy to argue. All she wanted to do was go for a walk. But Nelson didn't think she needed a walk at all.

"You need to stay here," he said firmly.

Jennifer didn't listen. She put on her shoes and grabbed a light jacket just in case it started to rain.

She was going for a walk, but she wasn't going to be able to go alone. Nelson followed her downstairs, continuously yelling at her and blaming her for everything that was wrong with his life.

"You're nothing but a son of a bitch," he yelled at her.

A woman walking toward them crossed the street to the opposite side, when she realized the severity of the argument happening in front of her.

"Leave me alone, Nelson," Jennifer snapped. "I want to be alone."

But he wouldn't turn back. He continued on, determined to make her listen. But the more he yelled, the more she ignored him. And the more infuriated he became.

"I've got something in the back of my head that I'm going to take to my grave," he blurted out.

Jennifer stopped dead in her tracks and turned to face him.

"What the hell . . . do you . . . mean by that! Are you saying that you killed the girls?"

He was silent long enough for Jennifer to think he was serious. Her rage was intensifying by the second.

"What are you, crazy? Why would I hurt my own youngsters?" he said. And that was it. He turned away and left her alone.

She had questions as to why he didn't take better care

of the girls at Little Harbour, but it was the first time she'd ever wondered if he could have actually drowned them. She quickly shook off the thought. As much as he tried to hurt her, he surely didn't have it in him to take the lives of his own daughters.

But it wouldn't be the last time she would hear him say those words.

52

"Hello, come on in," Jennifer said to Chris and Lori, who were standing at her door. She knew they worked with victim services, and she wondered why they were here today.

"We were wondering if you were free to come up to the office for a while," said Lori. "We just wanted to make sure everything was okay, and to have a chat."

"Sure, just give me a minute to get ready," said Jennifer.

Meanwhile, Chris had already arranged for Nelson to go to the police station.

Jennifer got into the car and headed to the office. She was hoping this wouldn't take too long. She was exhausted. She didn't feel like answering any more of their questions, and for the most part she no longer had any answers. The days between the girls' deaths and their funeral were fuzzy. She wasn't sure if it was the shock or the little white pills, but there weren't many memories. The memories she did have were scattered pieces, like snapshots of time.

"How are you coping?" said Lori.

"I'm okay, but I just feel tired and confused most of the time," she responded.

"What about Nelson?"

"Well, he's been having plenty of his moods, but things are okay, I guess," Jennifer said.

"Do you feel safe, though?" asked Lori. "We need to make sure you are okay. Is there enough food at the apartment?"

"Well, we do need groceries, but I guess Nelson will get some in a couple days."

"We're going to be keeping a close eye on you, Jennifer," said Lori. "Just to make sure you are all right. Is that okay?"

"Yes it is," said Jennifer. "I'll take whatever help I can get."

"There's something else." Lori looked uncomfortable in her chair. "Jennifer, we found the girls' car seats up at the dump the day after the incident at Little Harbour. We believe Nelson brought them up there that same night.

"Also, we found pictures of Krista and Karen," Lori continued. "We found a lot of pictures of them. We're not sure why Nelson threw them out, but the police have them now. He even threw away the negatives. I promise we'll make sure you get them back."

Jennifer was stunned. How could he throw away their pictures? She felt like he was trying to wipe away their memory, but she put it in the back of her mind and continued on.

Jennifer was aware that Nelson had been meeting with the police, but she had no idea what he was telling them. Nor was she interested in Nelson. The girls were all she could think of. But throwing away their pictures? What was his reason?

Lori gathered up Jennifer's coat and helped her out to the car. The two of them drove quietly back to the apartment, and they headed upstairs.

Nelson was already home from the police station. There was no trouble hearing his yelling echoing down the stairwell.

"Those sons of bitches. They got her. The police got her, and they won't be bringing her home," he was yelling.

Jennifer opened the door. Nelson stopped and turned. He looked at Jennifer, then his focus shifted toward Lori.

"You're a bunch of bastards! You took my wife, and I didn't know nothing!" he yelled. "You're nothing but a bunch of arseholes."

53

Why?

"Why would you throw away the girls' pictures, Nelson?" Jennifer was fuming.

"They're only pictures," he replied, without taking his eyes away from the television. "What odds."

"What odds?" said Jennifer. "This doesn't make sense! You know how much those pictures meant to me."

Suddenly, Jennifer was overcome by longing. She was longing to be with her girls.

"Take me to the graveyard," she demanded. "That's the least you could do."

"I'm not going up there today," he said. "Just look outdoors, it's pouring."

"I don't care. I want to go now."

Jennifer grabbed her jacket and waited at the door. She nearly leapt down the stairwell. For reasons she couldn't explain, there was an urgency to be with them.

She felt relief just to be in the car and driving toward them, even though it was not the kind of day you'd find anyone hanging around the cemetery. The wind was up, and as they got closer to the cemetery she saw flashes of lightning and heard the thunder. But none of that mattered. Nothing would stop her from visiting their graves this day.

As they turned into the graveyard, Jennifer asked Nelson, "Are you coming with me?"

"I'm staying here," he replied.

Jennifer got out of the car and started walking toward the little white crosses, which were the only things she had left to bring her closer to her lost children. The rain, which had been pouring from the heavens moments ago, began to subside. There was no lightning. No thunder.

She no longer cared about her clothes, or her hair. She knelt on the wet ground and wept. She cried so that she could make all this go away. She cried so that she could have her children back in her arms where they belonged. Not here, out in this terrible weather, with no one to comfort them. If they couldn't be here, she wanted to be with them.

Time stood still for her this particular visit. So did the weather. When Jennifer looked up from the little grave markers, she could see Nelson sitting behind the wheel of the car. Waiting.

Jennifer stood and walked toward him, and when she got within a few feet of the car, the rains began to crash down again. As soon as she sat in the car, there was a clap of thunder that made her shiver.

She believed it was a message. The girls had cleared the way for her to come visit that day.

54

"Why don't we get out of town for the day?" he said. "I've got enough money to drive into St. John's."

"What are we going to do in there?" Jennifer asked.

But Nelson never really answered the question. Instead, he said he was going to gas up the car. "I'll be back in a while, so be ready to go."

Jennifer wasn't really up to travelling, but she didn't ask any more questions. She just did as she was told. It had only been a few weeks since the girls had died, and already there was no food in the house. There wasn't even enough money to wash clothes at the laundromat downstairs. The Salvation Army had brought food a few days ago, but that was gone. People from all over had sent money to the funeral home, but Jennifer had no idea what had happened to it. And she didn't have the strength to worry about it all, because the pain had become too much to bear. It didn't matter where she was anymore, because her children weren't there.

She packed a small bag.

"Do you have enough money to go to St. John's?" Jennifer asked. "This morning you didn't have enough to give me for laundry."

"I have money," he said. "Don't worry about it."

Jennifer wasn't surprised. It certainly wasn't the first time Nelson had a secret stash of money she didn't know about. She got in the car, and as they drove, there wasn't much in the way of conversation. Jennifer had taken a sedative, and she was content to watch the world slide by through the side window. Nelson wasn't in the mood for talking, either. There were times when she wondered why he wanted to make the four-hour drive to St. John's, but she didn't have the energy to try and retrieve an answer from him.

When they finally arrived in the city, Nelson drove straight to the Avalon Mall. Jennifer assumed there was something he was looking for, until he drove to an empty parking area and parked their car in the middle of the empty spaces.

Instead of getting out of the car, he did something she didn't expect.

"I don't have any money," he admitted.

"Well, what the hell are we going to do now?" she said. "You mean to tell me we're out here with no money? Not even enough for gas to get back?" she questioned.

Nelson didn't say anything. He just sat staring straight ahead, and Jennifer had never felt so alone in the world.

Jennifer drifted in and out, until it was finally dark. She reclined her seat and went to sleep.

When she woke the next morning, she nearly had to fight for her breath. The air in the car was hot with the morning sun, but it was also humid. She had never felt so messed up. She couldn't get the window down fast enough.

There wasn't enough air to make her feel better, and she badly needed to stretch her legs. Not to mention the fact that she really needed to find a washroom. But the mall was still closed.

She reached for the door handle.

"Don't touch it," said Nelson.

Jennifer could tell right away, by the look in his eyes, he hadn't slept at all. She could see the stress in his face, and she knew there was something serious going on in his mind.

"You're staying aboard this car," he said. "I'm not getting out, and you're not getting out, either."

Jennifer didn't believe he could last like this much longer. The car was uncomfortable and they were hungry. So she didn't say a word. She waited and watched as the sun climbed higher in the sky, and eventually people began making their way to and from the mall.

It was the only thing she could do. She watched the teenagers waiting at the bus stop. None of them seemed to be in a hurry to go anywhere, and she kind of admired them for it. But her daughters would never get to be teenagers. They would never get to hang out like these kids. Then there were the women. Women carrying bags of items, some pushing strollers, and some with their children skipping along at their sides. It was too much for her. She snuggled down in the seat. The hunger finally passed and she fell asleep.

When she woke, it was nighttime. Theirs was the only car in the mall parking lot.

Maybe now would be a good time to get out and stretch. But no, Nelson wasn't about to let that happen. When Jennifer looked over, he was sitting up and looking straight ahead.

For the first time since they had parked here, Jennifer was genuinely beginning to worry about what he had planned. He couldn't keep her here forever. What was the point of this? Was he going to starve her to death?

She wiped everything from her mind, reclined her chair, and went back to sleep.

The next time she woke up, it was daylight again. This time there were people all around, but she didn't have the strength to watch them. She felt sick, and the situation was getting desperate. Fortunately, she no longer felt the urge to pee, but she wondered what her body was doing with the fluid.

"Nelson," she said. "Let me call someone in here. Mom's got two brothers and a sister who live in here. Let me call them, and they'll help us out."

"No," was all he said.

"They will give us money for gas," she pleaded. "Let's at least call them for some food, or to let us wash up."

The next morning, Jennifer was starting to feel very sick. "Nelson, can I at least get into the back seat where I can stretch out?" she asked. She knew that if she didn't soon get food she would end up in the hospital, or worse. She barely had the strength to move.

Nelson got out of the car and opened the door for her to climb into the back.

The feeling of her feet on the pavement felt so good she felt like running, but she knew there was no way she'd have the strength. So she lay on the back seat and watched Nelson.

He was thinking about something. She was sure of that. And whatever it was, it was really making him anxious. Jennifer wondered if he had even closed his eyes to nap for the past four days.

But as she watched him, she noticed that his head was dropping forward from time to time. She suspected he was more tired than she thought. Suddenly, she saw his head slump forward. He was asleep.

Quietly, she opened the door. Her hand trembled as it grasped the plastic lever. She was very weak, and she hoped she wouldn't have to go far for help, because she didn't know if she was strong enough to stand upright.

She paused as her feet rested flat on the pavement, and then, with a push, she did stand. And as she looked inside at Nelson, she realized that he was not going to wake up any time soon.

She looked around the parking lot. Desperate. What could she do?

Suddenly, she spotted an older man who looked to have a friendly face. He had spotted Jennifer first. With the way he was staring, she wondered what she must look like. His jaw literally dropped as she walked toward him. For a moment she thought he was going to run.

"Hi," she said. "I'm really hungry. I've been here in this car for the past four days, and my husband won't let me leave. I . . . I've been looking at that Chinese restaurant right there. Can you go get me something to eat?"

Jennifer wasn't sure if the man wanted to help her, or if he was afraid of her. But she'll never forget the way he looked at her that day.

"I don't have any money on me right now," he said. "But I have to come back here at seven o'clock tonight. When I do, I will bring food for you."

Jennifer struggled back to the car. The man watched as she got into the back seat and lay down.

Little did she know, the police had been searching for her and Nelson for the past four days. When the man called the police that afternoon to report what he had witnessed, it didn't take long for them to show up on the scene.

Jennifer was taken to the police station in the first cruiser. Nelson was put in handcuffs and put in another car.

At the police station she was given food and a chance to wash up. With the first couple bites of her hamburger,

Jennifer thought she was going to be sick. The whole ordeal had been a lot harder on her body than she realized. Then the police officers sat down to give her an update.

"Nelson had a couple of seizures while we were on our way here from the parking lot," the officer informed her. "We have taken his driver's licence, so you're going to have to drive him back to Gander. That is, if you're comfortable going back with him."

"Are you sure you are feeling well enough?" the officer asked.

"Yes," she said, "but I don't have any money to buy gas."

The officers gave her enough money to make it home. When she was walked toward the car, Nelson was already sitting in the passenger seat.

For a moment, Jennifer dreaded getting back into the car. But she knew the police were keeping an eye on them, so she got in.

Nelson was reading a letter the police had given him.

"How did the police find us there?" he asked. "Was it you? Did you tell them?"

Jennifer denied finding help, and for the next four hours she listened endlessly to Nelson complaining. He was furious that his driver's licence had been taken because of the seizures. And he blamed Jennifer.

55

In Gander, Jennifer was grateful for her first night's sleep on a real bed. The next morning, her legs were still a little sore, but she was eating normally again, and she was well on the way to recovering from her ordeal in St. John's.

But getting out of bed was also a problem for another reason. The girls were on her mind all the time.

Later that day, Jennifer was back to juggling the household once again. She was boiling potatoes for lunch, but periodically running down to the basement to do laundry at the same time. On her last trip up from the laundry room, she discovered her dinner was starting to burn.

She shut off the pot, and at the same time there was a knock on the door. Nelson was lying on a mattress on the floor, and he turned to see who it was.

"Good morning, Constable Trainor," Jennifer said. She had met the officer a few times before.

"Good morning," he said. "Looks like you're cooking some lunch?"

"She was," said Nelson. "Until she burned it up."

"Don't worry about it," he said. "We need to talk to both you guys, if you're able. Nelson, there's a car downstairs waiting for you, and Jennifer can come with me." Jennifer got into the cruiser and they headed to the police station. Inside, they walked up the stairs to what Constable Trainor called the Major Crime Unit. It was a section of the police station that Jennifer had never been to before. She didn't know where Nelson was.

"Before we discuss any of this, you're having something to eat," said the officer. "What would you like us to pick up for you?"

Within a few minutes a young woman returned with a bag of McDonald's. The smell of the fries made Jennifer realize just how hungry she was. When the bag was opened, she devoured its contents in a hurry. She had never tasted anything so good. There were times she had to slow down simply because she felt like her body might reject such a big meal so quickly. It was a heck of a lot better than the potatoes she had left at home.

"Jennifer, we don't want you to go back with Nelson," he said. "We think he killed your daughters, and he's probably going to be charged. Our fear is that he is dangerous, and that he might try to do something to you."

It was a thought that had crossed Jennifer's mind

several times after the death of the girls. But one she quickly abandoned to protect her own sanity. She had also tried her best to forget what he had done in St. John's. More importantly, she tried to bury thoughts of what his intentions were.

Suddenly, Nelson's words came to her mind. *I have something in the back of my mind that I'm going to take to my grave.*

There were times she wondered why he didn't try harder to save Krista that day. Why didn't he wrap her up, or do anything before he came back to Gander?

Now, she understood exactly what the officer was saying. It all made sense. At that moment, she wanted nothing else to do with Nelson Hart. Husband or not, she was going to get away from him.

She wasn't sure what to think about her own life anymore. But she knew that she was safe in the hands of the police, and she would have food.

"We're going to buy you some supplies, and then we're going to bring you somewhere safe," said Constable Trainor. "We've been talking to your sister in Prince Edward Island, and it's fine if you stay there. Are you okay with that?"

Jennifer agreed, and in no time an officer showed up with all kinds of personal items she would need for the trip.

"We're going to bring you to Corner Brook tonight, where you can stay with your sister. Then you'll catch the ferry to the mainland at Port aux Basques in the morning."

They jumped into a big SUV, and the officers made her lie down on the back seat of the police cruiser to make sure Nelson wouldn't see her as they left the station. They drove straight to the apartment. She didn't own any luggage, so Jennifer began to round up all her belongings in garbage bags.

But when the officers looked in on her, they discovered that what she was packing included all the items belonging to Karen and Krista.

"That's going to be a lot to have to carry with you," the officer stated. "Are you sure you wouldn't be better off leaving it here?"

"I'm not leaving the girls' stuff here, because he might do something with it," Jennifer snapped back.

So, with $60 in her pocket, and all her possessions in the back of the vehicle, Jennifer left Nelson behind.

56

The police cruiser rolled into her sister's driveway, and Penny was there waiting in the front window. The police officers helped her carry her belongings inside, and with a few instructions, they wished her luck and were on their way.

Penny hugged her sister. "I'm glad you're here, Jennifer. Everything's going to be okay," she said. "Things will get better."

For the first time since the girls' deaths, Jennifer actually felt like she might be able to start getting her life back on track. The two sisters made their way downtown to the social services offices, where the arrangements were already made. There was some spending money for Jennifer, as she travelled to Prince Edward Island, and two vouchers for the cost of the ferry.

Jennifer had told the police early on that she would not be travelling on the ferry alone. Not only was she nervous about the trip, but she couldn't handle the sight of water anymore. The other voucher was for Penny's return trip.

The next morning, she and Penny were up before the sun, and on their way to the ferry. The last time Jennifer had made the drive to Port aux Basques, the girls were in the back seat, and it was a much happier time. As they drove along the highway, Jennifer remembered that particular drive.

By ten o'clock they had arrived and were finally ready to board.

"Penny, promise me we won't have to look at the water, okay?" said Jennifer. "I just can't take it." They managed to make the rest of the trip by sitting in the ship's interior. Jennifer and her sister chatted and watched the people passing by. Others were napping, while several people were having an early morning party at the bar.

When they got off the big ferry in Nova Scotia, her mother was there, along with her brother-in-law. They drove for several hours through the scenic countryside of Cape Breton, so far away from her home. So far away from the graves in which she took comfort.

But she knew in her heart this was the right thing to do. What if Nelson had really killed the girls? And what about the scene at the mall? Was he trying to make her so weak that he would kill her, too?

She tossed the ideas back and forth in her mind. At the same time, she tried not to think of the little white crosses where she longed to be.

Suddenly, the car was slowing down, and she looked ahead to see where they were. It was another ferry. They were getting ready to cross to Prince Edward Island.

"Mom, I don't want to see the water," she said. Fortunately, for Jennifer this ferry ride would be a short one, and she didn't have to get out of the car.

When they got to her sister's in Prince Edward Island, her three nieces and nephews came running to meet her. She was happy to see them, but she still felt very far from home.

Her sister's house was crowded. It was a three-bedroom bungalow. Living there were the four children, Susan and her husband, and her mother and her boyfriend, Pat.

Jennifer would be sleeping on a blow-up mattress on the living room floor. It wasn't the most ideal of accommodations, but she was convinced this was the best, and safest, place for her. Her family all agreed: they didn't trust Nelson one bit, and they wanted her with them.

She settled in as best she could, but her heart longed to visit the girls' graves. It had only been a month since they died.

"She's not here," Jennifer overheard Susan on the phone. "Well, I don't know who told you that," she said into the receiver. "But Jennifer is not with us."

The phone call had gotten Jennifer's full attention. "Who was that?"

"Nelson's mother. She says she knows you're staying here, but I didn't tell her anything," said Susan.

Jennifer settled back down into her chair. She didn't have the energy to deal with this right now, and she hoped that would be the last phone call. But the caller wouldn't give up easily, and Jennifer knew that all too well.

She called another week later, and again her sister refused to give any information. Jennifer could guess what Nelson's mother would say. She could already hear her defending her son, telling Jennifer that he didn't hurt the girls. He would never hurt her, and she would be best off with Nelson.

But Jennifer was too tired to listen to it. And living in a busy house also helped keep her mind off Nelson and his mother as well.

That is, until one evening when she was sitting in the living room. The kids were huddled in front of the television, and she and Susan were having a cup of tea.

"There's someone there!" screamed Jennifer. "There was someone looking in the window!"

Panic ensued. Her brother-in-law and Pat took off running to see if they could find the person, but they found no one.

"It was probably someone on their way home from the

bar down the road," said her mother. "But I'm not taking any chances on what Nelson Hart would do to get next to Jennifer."

She called the police, who in turn called the RCMP in Gander.

The next morning, they received a call that worried the entire family.

"We've tried tracking Nelson down," the officer said over the phone. "We've looked everywhere, but he's nowhere to be found. You need to stay safe, and don't worry, we'll be keeping a close eye on your house."

Jennifer was surprised to see patrol cars passing their house the next day, keeping a steady watch. She left the next afternoon to go down to the local grocery stores, and five police cars passed her along the way.

If nothing else, she knew that they were protecting her, but it also showed her just how seriously the police were taking the situation. Their diligence showed her how much they believed Nelson had the potential to be dangerous.

That evening, there was some relief for Jennifer's family, after a call came in from the police. Nelson was staying with his mother. Jennifer could relax for now.

Constable Trainor continued to stay in touch with Jennifer, to keep her posted on any new developments and to see how she was doing.

"Nelson called here the other night," she said. "The caller identification was from his mother's house, but whoever was on the other end didn't speak. His mother would have said something, so we think it was Nelson."

"Well, you're safe where you are," the officer reassured her. "I've been told by the police in Charlottetown that they are keeping a very strong presence in your area."

But despite being safe, Jennifer wasn't happy. She wanted her own bed. She wanted to be in Newfoundland. She wasn't particularly comfortable being on the mainland.

But most of all, she missed being able to visit Karen and Krista's graves. She wanted to be home. She was a grieving mother who couldn't even visit her daughters' graves. It was torture.

On December 19, Jennifer, her mother, and her stepfather, Pat, got in the car and headed for home. But Jennifer wouldn't get to Gander right away. They went to her mother's home on the south coast, nearly three hours away.

Though she was glad to be back on the island, she still wasn't content.

Christmas came and went uncelebrated, and she longed to be able to visit their graves every day.

After Christmas, two RCMP members dropped in to St. Alban's for a visit.

"So, how are you doing?" asked Constable Trainor, who was genuinely concerned.

"I'm okay, but I want to be back in Gander, where I can be close to the girls' graves," she told him.

The officer looked around the one-bedroom trailer. It was small, and Jennifer had created a makeshift bedroom in the living area. There was barely enough room here for two, let alone three people.

"I can see that," he said. "I guess you need your own space. If you are up to it, we can arrange for you to stay in a transition house in Gander. That way you will be safe from Nelson, and you might feel better."

Jennifer wasn't thinking of Nelson at all. She just wanted to be home, and their words made her want to leave right away. She had never longed to be somewhere as much as she wanted to be at the cemetery at that moment.

57

It wasn't long before Jennifer was settled in back at the transition house. A place she had become too familiar with over the years. She knew the workers, and there was usually someone staying there who she knew as well. Most of the women who left their husbands because of abuse usually ended up back in their marriages, no matter how bad things got. And no matter how much their husbands promised to change, the abuse always seemed to start again. And the women would eventually end up back in the transition house time after time. Jennifer supposed she was really no different than the rest of these women.

But this time she didn't care. She was relieved to be closer to her daughters' graves. She was also relieved to have her own bed and her own closet.

Today she wasn't in the mood to nap, but there was nothing better to do than to lie on her bed and enjoy the space. The two plastic tubs containing all of Karen and Krista's belongings sat in the closet. She sized up the tubs that she had carried with her through the entire move. She had carried them from one province to another and home again. She wondered how many times she would have to carry this stuff through the rest of her life. Right now, that didn't matter. She'd carry it to the moon if she had to. It was also in the back of her mind that a substantial amount of their belongings was still in the hands of the RCMP. She prayed those belongings were in safe hands. There were pictures and baptism certificates, there were some toys, and a lot of the girls' clothes. The police assured her that they would take care of the items. If not for the police, the pictures might never have been recovered from the garbage. For that, she was grateful.

"Jennifer!" yelled a voice from down the hallway. "Phone!"

A phone call? Jennifer wondered who it could be.

"How are ya, my dear?" asked the familiar voice.

Jennifer wasn't prepared to hear her mother-in-law At the same time, she wasn't surprised.

"I'm okay," Jennifer said.

"Would you like to go out for a bit of lunch?"

Jennifer agreed, even though she knew where this would lead. She also knew the police wanted her to stay away from Nelson.

She made the walk down to the local Chinese restaurant, where Jennifer sat down, and her mother-in-law began to tell her everything that had happened since she had left. How Nelson had missed her. She went on to say that she didn't believe her son was capable of ever hurting her children, and that Jennifer belonged back with her husband.

On the way back to the transition house, Jennifer wasn't sure what to think. But in the end, she had agreed to meet Nelson. To talk.

They met at the local coffee shop, where Nelson wasted no time trying to assure Jennifer everything his mother had said was true. He loved those girls.

"Look at how hard the last few months have been," he said to her. "You need to have your own place again. I still have the apartment. Come home."

And as she had dozens of times before, Jennifer went home.

58

"The girls need a headstone for their graves," Jennifer told Nelson. They were sitting in the car, and Jennifer had just spent the past hour fixing up the graves, placing new flowers and teddy bears. Nelson had waited in the car.

"We don't have that kind of money," he said.

"Well, why don't we go away to work?" she asked. "The fish plant in PEI is hiring, and the pay is pretty good."

It didn't take long to convince Nelson to move. He felt like everyone was watching him these days, and he quickly agreed. But they weren't able to leave as quickly as they would have liked. The first thing they needed was reliable transportation. For a few hundred bucks, they bought another car. It needed some work, but within a week it was registered and ready for the trip.

So the couple packed up their few belongings once again. They were making their second move to Prince Edward Island, but this time without the girls.

"How much money do you have for the trip?" Jennifer asked Nelson. "If there isn't enough, we should go down to social services to make sure we can get some help once we get there."

"I've got plenty of money," he reassured her.

What Jennifer didn't know was, even though he had enough to make it to Prince Edward Island, that was about the extent of his so-called wealth.

"You can both start tomorrow morning at six," said Mr. Gillingham. He was the manager at the plant, and it was no time before he had hired them both. It was a busy time of year for lobster processing, and he assured them there'd be plenty of overtime.

Jennifer was thrilled. "If we work overtime, that will get us closer to buying the headstone sooner." Jennifer had been on the road the entire day, but she was nearly skipping with excitement as they left the fish plant.

Nelson didn't say anything as they got in the car.

"We should go and try and find a hotel for tonight, and we'll look for an apartment tomorrow," she said. Jennifer was exhausted from the long day, and she knew 6:00 a.m. would arrive before she knew it. She had hoped to stay with her sister. But when the family found out Nelson was with her, she was no longer welcome.

Nelson didn't have much to say about their jobs or finding a place to stay for the night. He just wanted to drive around for a while and check out the area.

Jennifer began to worry something was wrong. Perhaps he was having one of his moods. Since they had gotten back together, things had been going fairly smoothly. But from past experience, she also knew that could change very quickly.

"We can't afford a hotel," he told her.

"What do you mean?" she asked. "Where are we going to stay? I'm not just staying with anyone at all. We're not in Newfoundland now, and I don't trust people up here."

She sat in silence, waiting to see what he was going to do, but he continued to drive.

When the sun started to go down, he pulled into a grocery store parking lot. But instead of stopping in front, he drove around to the back of the building. He shut the car off.

"Why are you stopping? We shouldn't be back here!" Jennifer protested. "There could be dangerous people around, Nelson."

"Well, we can't afford a hotel, so this is where we're sleeping," he said.

Jennifer's heart began to beat out of her chest. She was terrified. The mainland wasn't like Newfoundland. People were a little bolder, and a lot scarier for her. She'd heard about the crimes on the mainland, and she did not want to be in this parking lot for the entire night.

But before she knew it, Nelson was dozing off in the driver's seat.

She was alone. She was scared.

It would be a long night. She never closed her eyes for a second. She remained upright in her seat and watched every passing car, expecting the worst with each set of headlights. In her mind, she believed she and Nelson would be robbed or killed before the night was over, and there was no way she could sleep in such a state of anxiety.

Yet Nelson slept. He slept until Jennifer saw the sky begin to brighten in the east. He slept until the clock read 5:30 a.m.

Jennifer nudged him awake. "Come on," she said. "It's time to go to work."

It was going to be a long day, but Jennifer didn't care. The thought of finally buying a headstone kept her going. And it wasn't just the promise of being able to mark her daughters' graves properly. She found her time at the plant took her mind off Karen and Krista, at least for most of the day. In fact, she enjoyed the day so much that, when five o'clock came, she volunteered to work a few extra hours.

Nelson, however, didn't want the overtime. He left and agreed to come back and pick her up later at nine.

The time passed quickly for Jennifer, who was giving it all she had. But when the time came to start putting things away for the night, her thoughts turned to Nelson. She was so tired. She hadn't slept properly in days.

How could she sleep another night in that car? In that parking lot? She knew there was still no way she would be able to sleep. Not tonight, or for the next two weeks, for that matter.

Two weeks is exactly how long it would take before they would get their first paycheque, and an apartment.

For two weeks, the car was her home.

59

When Jennifer thought she couldn't take another night without sleep, the Salvation Army came to her rescue once again. They had found room for her and Nelson at a bed and breakfast in Souris.

The landlady was Margaret McDonald, and they became immediate friends. Almost right away, the McDonalds agreed to give Jennifer and Nelson an apartment, even though they wouldn't have all the rent money for a couple of weeks.

"I've got a basement apartment that's perfect for you two," said Mrs. McDonald. "I'll do you this favour, and perhaps if we need some help around the house you could give us a hand?"

It was the perfect arrangement, and the room was comfortable. For the first few days, Jennifer was so tired she found it hard to get out of the bed. But she did. She also continued to work long hours in order to save.

Jennifer was rarely around the apartment. Nearly every night she worked overtime. Each hour she worked, she believed she was one hour closer to buying the headstone. She didn't know where Nelson was going each night, but he obviously had no desire to work overtime. It was unfortunate, because Jennifer knew that with two good incomes they would be well off.

But today, as usual, he had left early and had promised to pick Jennifer up at finishing time, around nine o'clock. Today was payday, and Jennifer hoped Nelson hadn't been out wasting money when they still owed the McDonalds the rent money. She was looking forward to her first pay, and she headed downstairs to the office to pick it up before she left. There was no one there. Everyone was gone home for the night, so she would have to wait until tomorrow to pick up her money.

Back at home, she explained the situation to Mrs. McDonald, who was more than understanding. She didn't mind waiting a few extra hours for her to pay.

The next morning at work, Jennifer made the office her first stop.

"Good morning," she said to the office manager. "I meant to pick up my paycheque yesterday," she explained. "But by the time I left last night, the office was closed."

The clerk pulled out a drawer and a stack of envelopes. She began to flick through them and suddenly stopped.

"Your husband is the big guy with dark hair, right?" the clerk asked. "He asked for your cheque yesterday afternoon."

Jennifer was disheartened once again. She wanted that money so badly. At least Nelson couldn't cash it without her.

At break time, she found Nelson drinking a Pepsi in the break room.

"Nelson, you didn't tell me you picked up my cheque yesterday," she stated.

"Oh, I forgot," he said. He pulled the cheque out of his jeans pocket. "You sign this, Jennifer, and I will get it cashed. Then you'll have the money after work."

Jennifer looked at the amount on the front of the paper and smiled. She was satisfied with the pay, and it gave her the courage to keep going. In no time she would be picking out the most beautiful headstone she could find. The little crosses weren't enough to represent her daughters, and she couldn't wait to go home to pick out the marble headstone.

She scribbled her name across the back of the cheque and headed back to work.

That night, Nelson was there at his usual time waiting outside.

"Whew, what a long day," she said as she fell into the passenger seat. Her feet were burning, but she felt satisfied with what she had accomplished.

Nelson pulled away from the fish plant and headed for home.

"First thing we have to do is pay the McDonalds their rent," she said. "Did you cash my cheque? When we get home, you give me the $300 and I'll bring it upstairs."

"Why don't we wait to pay them?" asked Nelson.

"We're already late! You have to give me that money," she yelled.

At home, Nelson again argued that the McDonalds didn't need the money right away. Jennifer insisted until, finally, he passed over the $300 from his own cheque.

After she had brought the money upstairs, she got undressed and showered. She climbed into bed and quickly fell asleep, forgetting that Nelson hadn't given her any of the money she had worked so hard for.

Several times through the week, she asked him to give her the money.

"I'm holding on to it," he would say. "It's safer with me."

But little by little, Jennifer realized that, each night as she worked overtime, Nelson was gambling. Gambling away the headstone she wanted for her daughters.

It wasn't long before she decided there was no point in working overtime anymore. She and Nelson moved out of the basement apartment and into a house out on Souris Line. It was remote compared to most of the places where they had lived. There were no stores within walking distance, and Jennifer missed spending time with the McDonalds. She wasn't exactly looking forward to spending more time alone with Nelson, either. He was gambling, and then there were the moods. He had also become convinced he was sick, perhaps even dying.

A couple of days after they had moved into the house, she stood in the window watching his car as he pulled into the long driveway. He turned off the engine and sat in the car with his head on the steering wheel for several minutes. Jennifer knew it was a sign something was wrong. Once he was inside, there came an announcement.

"I've only got a few months to live," he sobbed. Nelson was crying like a baby at the kitchen table.

"I gave the doctor a false name and told him I just moved from Newfoundland so I didn't have insurance. That way, I figured Mom wouldn't be able to tell the doctor what to say."

Jennifer had heard this before. Every time Nelson went to the doctor by himself, he would come out with the news that he was dying.

"Let me go to the doctor with you to see if there's something more that I can find out," she said.

Reluctantly, he agreed. Two days later, she drove into town with him, but he didn't want her in the office.

When he came out, it was the same story.

"Well, what did he say?" she asked.

"Nothing," Nelson mumbled.

The two of them began a silent drive back to the house. Jennifer watched him, unsure whether or not she should push to find out more about what the doctor had said. Finally, she couldn't take it anymore.

"Nelson, if there was anything wrong with you, you'd be dead by now," she snapped at him.

But instead of hearing his response, she only felt a swift, burning pain as the back of his fist made contact with her nose.

She felt her whole head tilt back with the blow and then forward. When her head fell forward, she watched a spray of blood fall all over her white blouse. Her ears were ringing and her vision was blurry. She'd never felt anything like it before. Her whole head was burning with pain.

But in those few seconds her pain turned to rage. She retaliated with every ounce of strength she could gather and struck him in the side of the head with the back of her hand.

She cried silently for the rest of the drive home. She didn't know what hurt more, her face from the blow or her hand from striking Nelson. She was glad they were living alone so she wouldn't have to explain this mess to anyone. In the rear-view mirror she saw the blood on her face. As soon as the car stopped, she ran inside. Now as she stood before her reflection, she realized the entire front of her white shirt was red. When she removed her shirt, she saw that there was so much blood it had even soaked through her bra.

The sink filled with blood as she washed her blouse and bra. It was then she noticed her hand had turned black and was starting to swell. She knew it was broken, but she didn't care at the moment. Even with the pain in her face and her hand, she just wanted to be alone. It was no good to call a doctor or the police. Searching for help would probably just bring on more fighting. Perhaps even another smack.

She managed to save her blouse from the massive bloodstains, and she had a long shower. From her closet she found another shirt that would have to do. These days there wasn't much to choose from in her closet. Most everything was old and worn.

Jennifer put her jeans on and looked out the window. Nelson's car was still sitting in front of the house.

She had to get out of here. Jennifer couldn't bear to look at him, and she was in no mood to put up with another one of his tantrums. So she left the house and, thankfully, he didn't bother her on the way out.

But that soon changed. Just as the house was nearly out of sight, she heard a car pulling up behind her, slowly. She knew who it was.

As she walked, he pulled up alongside her and rolled down his window.

"Where do you think you're going?" he yelled.

"I'm going for a walk, Nelson. Leave me alone."

"Get in the car!"

"No, Nelson, I'm going for a walk. Leave me alone," she repeated.

But the more she pleaded for him to leave, the more determined he was to follow her.

"I knows what's wrong with you," he said. "You want to be home in Newfoundland so you can go to the girls' graves. Right?"

Jennifer didn't answer. The car slowed down briefly, but when he pulled up alongside her again, Nelson had something in his hand.

"You see this money?" he said, waving a roll of bills around. "There's over a thousand dollars here. That's enough money to get back to Newfoundland. You want to go, don't ya?"

Jennifer stopped, and so did the car. "Two days ago I had to go to the Salvation Army to get food, and now you're telling me you got a thousand dollars!" she yelled. She was furious. He had told her there was no money. She couldn't even afford a sandwich to take to work for her long shift.

Eventually, the car pulled away. Jennifer figured he was headed to the bar, probably to spend most of her hard-earned money on the slot machines. Once he was out of sight, she turned around and headed for home.

Back in her kitchen, she felt lost. And very alone. There was no way she could call her sister, and the rest of her family were far away, back in Newfoundland.

She began to dial her mother's number. But she wasn't sure what to say. Everyone had warned her not to go back with Nelson, but she went back anyway. It was a cycle that just continued no matter how many times Jennifer's mind told her to stop.

"Hi, Mom. How's everything down there?"

"All is well, girl, how are you? How's work?" her mom asked.

"It's okay, I've been working a lot of hours, but I'm not sure if I have enough made to buy the girls' headstone yet."

"Let me guess," replied her mother. "Nelson is taking all the money again! Is that why you're phoning? Do you have anything to eat?"

"I'm okay, Mom," Jennifer lied. "But Nelson is having his moods again."

"I don't like the sounds of this. What happened?"

"He struck me today," Jennifer admitted.

Jennifer went on to tell her mother the story. She knew there was no one else she could tell, and she felt desperate to know that someone was there for her.

"I've had just about enough of him, I'll tell ya that," said her mother. "If anything else happens, you let me know."

60

The next day, Jennifer noticed a police car driving by the house while she was doing the morning's dishes. *At least they do come all the way out here*, she thought.

She and Nelson went to work, and later that afternoon they passed another cruiser parked near the beginning of their road. When they got home, another police car passed their driveway.

"I thinks they're watching me," said Nelson.

"Don't be foolish," Jennifer said. "There's probably something going on out here we don't know about. Not to mention, have you noticed how fast everyone seems to drive on this road? They could be just trying to catch speeders."

Jennifer opened up the refrigerator to try and figure out what she would cook for supper, but there wasn't much to choose from. A few potatoes would have to do until she could get to the food bank tomorrow.

She pulled the potatoes out of the cupboard, and Nelson turned on the television and flopped down on the couch. But no sooner had she begun peeling the potatoes when Nelson jumped up from the chair. It startled Jennifer.

"There they go again," said Nelson. "The police. I've had enough of this. Get your boots on. I'm going to show them not to follow me. I'll show them what it's like to be watched."

Jennifer put on her boots and almost had to run to keep up with Nelson as he headed toward the car.

She shut the door, and the car was already in motion. He was almost speeding when he finally caught up to the police car.

"I don't think this is a good idea," Jennifer told him. "You're going to piss them off."

"I'm the one that's pissed off," he said.

Nelson continued to stay close to the police car. When

the car signalled left, so did Nelson. In fact, he was following them right to the police detachment. The police car pulled into the parking lot, and the driver looked over at Nelson and Jennifer.

Nelson got out of the car first. The officer opened his door as Nelson walked toward him. Jennifer could see them exchange words, and then the officer made Nelson turn around. That's when she saw he was putting handcuffs on him.

They were both brought into the police station and put in a small interview room.

"Mrs. Hart, we want to talk to you about this situation with your husband here," said the officer. "First of all, we understand you were recently talking to your mother." Jennifer was shocked. Why were they saying this in front of Nelson?

"Did you explain to your mother that Nelson had assaulted you? Punched you in the face, to use the exact words?"

"I didn't say anything like that to my mother," Jennifer lied. She hoped Nelson couldn't tell she was lying.

The officer sat silently looking at Jennifer.

"Okay, that's enough for now, but we still need to ask you a few questions, Nelson," he said.

The two officers stood and waved Nelson outside, leaving Jennifer alone in the room. She was stunned. Why would they ask her that in front of him? Suddenly, the first officer walked back into the room and sat in front of Jennifer across the table.

"Why did you say you weren't talking to your mother?" he asked. "Do you know that she called us right after you told her that Nelson punched you in the face?"

"There is no way I would admit that here in front of Nelson," Jennifer snapped. "He'd go out of his mind, mad, if he knew I told Mom that. I was afraid he was going to slap me right there."

There was a look of realization on the officer's face.

"I'm sorry, Jennifer. I guess we could have been a little more considerate," he said. "So, is it true? Did he assault you that day?"

"Yes, he did," replied Jennifer.

"Well, he is going to be charged, and he'll have to go to court," said the constable. "But you need to be somewhere safe. Tonight you will be staying at the transition house. Tomorrow you'll be on a flight back to Newfoundland."

That night the police drove Jennifer back to the house, where she gathered up her few belongings. Most importantly, she got the two tubs containing Karen and Krista's precious belongings.

She made the police promise to have them returned to Newfoundland safely. Before Jennifer knew what was happening, she was back on the island.

61

She could hardly believe she was back in Newfoundland again.

After landing at Gander Airport, her mother and Pat picked her up and brought her to St. Alban's to stay with them.

And once again, the police secured a room at the transition house in Gander. She understood that Nelson had also moved back by now. But this time she would not be lured back to Nelson, because she longed for a place to call her home. This time she would have her own place.

With some help, Jennifer moved into a small basement apartment after being in the transition house for a little more than six weeks.

It wasn't much, but it was hers. It was comfortable, clean, and, most of all, peaceful.

Not long after, she got her first phone call.

"Nelson just wants to go for a coffee."

As she always did, eventually Jennifer gave in. She already felt defeated as she made her way to the local Tim Hortons. She knew Nelson was there waiting. And she also knew that once they began talking, it was only a matter of time and they would be together.

She made each step knowing that it was against the advice of the police. It was against the wishes of her own family. Everyone was convinced that he had killed Karen and Krista, and deep down Jennifer believed it, too.

"Hi," she said. Nelson was waiting for her at one of the tables. He had already purchased her a tea and some cookies. If there was one thing Nelson was good at, that was making amends.

But maybe. Just maybe, he had changed. Jennifer hoped.

62

"Come on in," she called. Jennifer had just made a fresh pot of coffee, and she was cooking up a meal of spaghetti.

She'd been living on her own now for the past month, and she was quite proud of the little home she'd made for herself on Corrigan Street. And although she had no intentions on getting back with Nelson, he was now visiting at least once a day.

Nelson opened the door and stepped inside. He took off his jacket and hung it on the doorknob. Jennifer was already busy plating their dinner.

"How did your day go?" she asked him.

"All right, I suppose. Mom's getting on my nerves, though," he said.

Jennifer knew that Nelson and his mother's relationship hadn't improved at all over the past few months. He often talked about how hard it was for them to get along.

"I need to get out of this town," he said. "I need a break from all this."

"What do you mean?"

"Mom is driving me crazy, and everywhere I go, people are looking at me strange," he said.

Jennifer knew it was true. Over the past several weeks he had shared stories about people making him uncomfortable. She'd even heard one story about a man at a local bar who punched him three times. Once for Jennifer, and twice for each of the girls. A part of her pitied him, even though her memories of being struck weren't far from her thoughts.

"Well, I won't be moving anymore," Jennifer said bluntly. "I'm not moving away from the girls' graves ever again."

"It doesn't have to be that far away," he said. "I'd be happy enough in Grand Falls, I think. At least nobody out there knows me."

Jennifer had no desire to move. Not even an hour away in Grand Falls. In fact, she didn't care to live with Nelson at all. But each day, he came by for a visit. He seemed to be a changed man. There were no moods, and he was mostly polite. Each day he told the same story about his uneasiness and worries, until finally Jennifer agreed to move once more.

She wasn't sure whether it was pity or love that put her back on the same old course. Back with Nelson.

63

During her time in her own apartment, Jennifer had at least managed to gather up some more furniture. So starting over in Grand Falls wasn't as difficult as it had been on the mainland.

She and Nelson moved the furniture into an older building on Lincoln Road, and she was hoping that this would be the time her life would change for the better. For weeks now there were no mood swings. The only time he seemed to have a problem was when she wanted to talk about Karen and Krista. It was a subject that Nelson avoided.

They carried their furniture up the stairs, and by that same evening Jennifer had unpacked enough for them to have their first night in a proper bed. But the next morning, Jennifer felt anything but rested.

"Did you hear that scratching?" she asked Nelson.

"No, I didn't hear anything."

"I'm sure I could hear rats running through the walls all night long," she said. "There was no way I was going to sleep."

"Oh, it's probably just some noise the neighbours are making."

Jennifer got up, showered, and dressed. Breakfast wouldn't be an issue since there was no food.

"We're going to have to get some groceries, Nelson," she called out as she was fixing her hair.

"Well, I've got some things I want to do first," he said.

Jennifer wasn't sure what he had in mind, but Nelson was ready to go.

"Maybe I could stay here while you do your work," suggested Jennifer.

"No, come on, let's go," he replied.

Jennifer hopped into the passenger side of the car. She wasn't able to drive the car, which was a five-speed stick-shift transmission.

From their building, Nelson drove in the opposite direction of the grocery stores, to a local hotel.

"What are we doing here?" she asked. "It's only quarter to ten in the morning."

Nelson didn't say anything. Jennifer got out of the car and followed him into the hotel. At first he tried to open the door of the lounge, but it was still closed.

He pointed to a couple of oversized chairs in the lobby. "We can wait over here."

Jennifer was really hoping this wouldn't take long. She was hungry, and they still needed groceries. She also knew what Nelson had in mind, and she was really hoping he wouldn't spend every cent they had.

As soon as the door to the bar opened, Nelson was out of his chair. He no longer even noticed Jennifer. He walked straight forward to a video terminal on the left. He handed Jennifer a dollar. "Go get me a Pepsi, will ya?"

Jennifer brought his drink back and placed it on the side of the video lottery terminal. Then she sat back at a table and waited.

She wasn't sure how much money he had put into the machine so far, but he was making minimum bets trying to win the bonus. She knew this was going to be a long day.

By lunchtime, she was getting anxious.

"Nelson, why don't you give me a ride home, and you can come back here," she said.

"No, stay here with me," he said. "I won't be much longer."

If she were able to drive the manual transmission, she probably would have left already. Instead, she was forced to wait.

By mid-afternoon, she figured she'd try once more.

"Come on, Nelson," she pleaded. "Let's go get something to eat."

This time he didn't respond, and Jennifer knew this wasn't a battle she could win.

"I'm walking home," she said.

"No, you're not," he said. "You'll stay here and wait for me. You don't have keys to the apartment, anyway."

"Well, give me the keys," she said.

He turned to give her a warning glare. "That's my apartment, and these are my keys," he snapped. "You can wait."

Nelson continued to play the machine until after midnight. Then he sat and watched the machines to see which ones had accumulated the biggest bonus. The plan was to come back in the morning as soon as the doors opened. That was his strategy for winning.

But for Jennifer there was no winning. She quickly realized that things had not changed at all. Now she was back with Nelson again, despite knowing the difference. Deep down she knew nothing would change. She knew there was a possibility she could be physically hurt. But here she was, doing exactly what she knew she shouldn't.

64

Jennifer poured herself a cup of tea while Nelson got his coffee. He used the last couple of slices of bread to make toast, and Jennifer got dressed. She was expecting the usual routine of hitting the bar so Nelson could try and grab the bonus off the machine. But Nelson had other plans today for the first time in weeks.

"Let's go for a drive to Lewisporte," he said. Jennifer wondered how he had money for gas when they didn't have a bite to eat in the house. But she didn't question it. She was just glad to get a break from sitting in the bar and watching Nelson playing the slots for hours on end.

Nelson didn't bother gassing up before they left Grand Falls–Windsor, and when they hit the highway she noticed the gas gauge was reading about a quarter tank. She assumed they would have enough to get out there.

But after a quick drive around the town of Lewisporte, Nelson was ready to head back. He pulled into the local gas station.

Jennifer stayed in the car and watched the dollars and cents roll away on the old pump. Fifty dollars in total. Nelson made his way into the gas bar, and Jennifer watched as he pushed the buttons on the debit machine.

He walked out and sat in the seat with a sigh.

"My debit card isn't working," he said.

Jennifer wasn't surprised. He started the car and started to pull away from the gas station.

"You can't leave!" she yelled.

"I told them I will come back tomorrow with the money."

But Jennifer knew he had no intentions of following through. And in the days and weeks ahead, the phone was constantly ringing. It was the owner of the gas station demanding his money.

"Nelson, you have to pay them for the gas," she pleaded. "If you don't, they will never stop calling. Let's go to the store, get a money order, and at least send them a payment."

But the payment wasn't enough.

A week later, Jennifer and Nelson were walking into the mall when they were approached by a man.

"Are you Nelson Hart?" he asked.

"Yes," said Nelson as he took the envelope from the guy. As soon as he looked down, Nelson knew what was in his hand. A summons to appear in court.

"You rotten son of a bitch," Nelson started to yell. He threw the envelope at the sheriff, screaming the whole time. "You won't see me in court, you fucker!"

After they left the mall, they headed down the busiest street in town when the flashing red and blue lights pulled up behind them.

Nelson was put in handcuffs and led to the police car.

"Can you take the car home?" the officer asked Jennifer.

"I can't drive a standard transmission," she replied.

So the police drove Jennifer back to the apartment while Nelson was taken to the detachment to wait for a court appearance.

Jennifer was home for about an hour when the phone rang. It was Nelson.

"I need for you or Mom to get me out of this!" he begged.

"There isn't anything either of us can do now," said Jennifer.

The next day, Nelson got his day in court, along with a year's probation.

65

Jennifer sat in the apartment. She was hungry, because last week's donation from the food bank had run out and they wouldn't be open again until tomorrow. The cupboards were bare except for a box of tea.

And even if there was food, now the only place to eat was on the coffee table. Nelson had sold the dining room table, opting instead to use the money to try and regain some of his losses from the slot machine.

Without a bed, they were sleeping on the floor, and each night Jennifer could hear the rats scurrying through the walls. She slept, fearing that one of them would wake her up by chewing on her face.

"Come on," said Nelson. "I'm going over to Dooley's."

"I don't want to go," she protested. "I'm sick of spending all my time at he bar."

"You are going!"

Jennifer could see one of his moods coming on, but she didn't care. She was fed up living like this.

"This is not your apartment, and you're not staying here." He walked up to her, face to face.

Jennifer could see the cold look in his eyes, and she felt his fist, and her feet came up off the floor. Suddenly, she was falling. The back of her head was the first part of her to strike the floor, and she could feel her entire body bounce back into the air. Her ears rang. But she knew from the look in his eyes that to stay on the floor only meant more trouble.

Even though the world went black for a moment, she jumped up and ran straight for the door. She fumbled with the doorknob and turned back for a moment. And in that moment all she saw was the knife in Nelson's hand. She ran down the hallway and looked back. Thank God he wasn't following.

Outside, she sat on the step. Waiting for the ringing in her ears to stop. She also felt dizzy, to the point where she resisted the urge to throw up.

Suddenly, the door burst open. It was Nelson. He walked with determination right past her, to his car, and climbed inside.

Jennifer could see him sitting behind the wheel fumbling with something. She couldn't tell what he had in his hands, so she backed up toward the building to a corner where he couldn't see her.

For the next five hours she sat on the step. She kept watching.

Finally, Nelson decided he'd had enough of the waiting game and opened the door of the building for Jennifer.

She followed him to the apartment, where he put the key in the lock and let her in.

66

A week later and Jennifer's head still hurt. In fact, she felt like something had cracked that day her head hit the floor. Yet she chose to keep it to herself, and she didn't bother going to the hospital.

But the one thing she couldn't handle anymore was sleeping with the sound of the rats.

"Hello, Harry," she said into the phone. "When is the new apartment going to be ready?" When the phone rang, she hoped that it was a call telling them they could move in earlier than expected.

"I've got some bad news," he said. "The guy who was living there is in the hospital. The problem is his family turned off the heat and the pipes have burst, flooding the apartment."

Jennifer was devastated. She could hardly wait to get out of this building.

"Can I come up and have a look?" she asked.

"Sure, but you'll see that this is going to require a lot of fixing up."

Jennifer was so anxious, she already had a plan in place. If she could do it, she was going to help in the cleanup to speed up the process.

"Come on in." Harry held the door for her and Nelson.

He was right, the carpet was sopping wet and the drywall was swollen and crumbling.

"I know how to do some plastering and painting," Jennifer proposed.

Harry was surprised and seemed a little unsure. But after some convincing, he told Jennifer to go ahead and pick up the supplies. He would dry the carpets out and she could do the rest.

Two days later and the carpets were dry enough to get to work. When she got to the apartment the new sheets of drywall were there waiting. But there were still a few things she would need.

"Nelson, can you give me a ride to the store?"

67

It was a mild day for February, and Jennifer was only wearing a light jacket. Nelson parked the car in front of the dollar store, and Jennifer set about to find everything she needed. Fixing up the apartment would be reward work. When she finished the repairs, Jennifer would get to pick out her own colours and have everything freshly painted. From the hardware section she found scrapers and putty knives. She also figured this would be the perfect place to get her paintbrushes, a tray, and some drop cloths for the carpet. With a freshly cleaned carpet, the last thing she wanted to do was to get paint splatter all over everything.

"Look Jennifer, look Jennifer. I got fifty dollars!" Nelson was skipping down the aisle like a child.

"I got fifty dollars. I got fifty dollars!"

"Okay, okay," she said. "Where did you get money like that?"

"There was a fellow in the parking lot." Nelson was trying to catch his breath. "He came right up to the car window. He's from Montreal, I could hardly understand a word he was saying. Anyway, he has a trucking company, and his sister drove a truck down here a while ago. He says she's a drug addict and an alcoholic. His mother is dying of cancer, and they want to get his sister home before she dies. Apparently she's on welfare here in Grand Falls, and he gave me fifty dollars to help him find her."

Jennifer wasn't sure what to think of it. It was easy money, that was for sure, but it was unlikely she'd get to see any of it.

"So, what do you have to do?" she asked.

"Well, his sister likes to gamble, so he wants me to go around to all the bars in town. He wanted me to go right away, but I told him I had to talk to you first," said Nelson.

Jennifer had her doubts, but getting Nelson out of her hair for a few hours would probably speed up her work. At least she didn't have to worry about him getting contrary with her.

"Give me a few more minutes and I'll be out," Jennifer said.

Jennifer picked up the rest of her supplies and waited in line for fifteen minutes before she was checked in. By the time she went outside, Nelson's new French friend was nowhere to be seen.

Jennifer got in the car.

"He's going to meet me up at the apartment," Nelson said.

They made the five-minute drive back to the apartment on Brown's Avenue. The first thing Jennifer noticed was the big black pickup sitting in the driveway. When they pulled into the driveway, a good-looking young man jumped out of the truck. Jennifer wasn't sure what to think. He was running toward the car before they even had a chance to park.

He came to Jennifer's side first and opened the door.

"You have good husband, you have good man," he said through a thick French accent. As Jennifer stood up, he hugged her. "I'm so glad your husband is going to help me find my sister."

Jennifer thought the man must be a maniac. He was so full of energy and eager to become friends.

Nelson hopped up into the truck with the French man named Steph. Jennifer watched them drive away, wondering what Nelson was getting himself into.

She went inside the apartment. There was a lot of work to be done, so she temporarily forgot about Nelson and the strange man.

It was a productive day. The two of them didn't get back until close to five o'clock.

"Hi, Jennifer," said Steph. He stood at the doorway, and Jennifer wasn't about to invite him in just yet. "Your husband was a great help today."

"Did you have any luck?" Jennifer asked.

"Not really," Nelson said. "I think we're going to be looking in Bishop's Falls tomorrow."

"I will give you a hundred this time," said Steph.

He shook Nelson's hand and told him to be ready for 9:00 a.m. Nelson agreed.

The next morning, Steph was knocking on the door at nine sharp. To Jennifer's surprise, Nelson was up, had eaten breakfast, and was eager to get on the move.

Nelson was out the door.

Jennifer spent the day putting the finishing touches on the plaster, and by late afternoon she was sizing up her handiwork. Now came the task of choosing her colours for the paint.

She was sanding down the drywall when the phone rang.

"How's the work going?" Nelson said on the other end of the phone. "Listen, there's no need to worry about supper. Steph says we're going to pick up something. See you soon."

Jennifer was surprised by Nelson's friendly demeanour. It was a welcome change from what she was used to. But she suddenly realized just how hungry she was. She'd had nothing to eat the entire day. In fact, she couldn't remember if she'd eaten yesterday, either.

When Nelson and Steph showed up at the door a little while later, there was no mistaking the smell of the pizzas. Her mouth watered at the smell.

The kitchen was small, and Steph set the three large pizzas down onto the tiny table. Jennifer and Steph sat while Nelson ate his dinner standing.

Jennifer had a lot of questions, but at the moment she was more interested in getting some food into her stomach. She put the first piece down in seconds, and then she rested to give her stomach a chance to settle.

"So there's no sign of your sister?" Jennifer asked.

Steph had one slice of pizza on his plate, but he had only taken one small bite. Jennifer realized that he had been watching her eat.

"No, but I'll find her," said Steph. "I'm in the middle of setting up business here. So I will be spending more time on the island."

Jennifer was trying to get used to the thick French accent. At the same time she was trying to listen, she couldn't get enough of the pizza. She couldn't stop eating even though she had questions.

"What about the truck your sister was driving?" Jennifer asked. "Didn't you look for that?"

"Oh, we found the truck," said Steph. "It's back in Montreal. You should work for us, Jennifer. We need a receptionist."

"Well, I don't have no degree in office work," said Jennifer. "I don't think I could do it."

"We could train you," he said. "We just need you to be there to open doors for our trucks."

"Yeah," said Nelson. "You'd be good at that, and we don't have any kids, so, you know, you'd be available all the time."

Jennifer started to slow down. Finally, she was starting to feel full. And then there was Steph. She couldn't understand why he kept staring at her with each mouthful of food she swallowed.

"Well," he said, standing up from the table. "This was wonderful. Nelson, you have been such a good help to me. Can I call you from time to time, when I need help?"

"Sure," said Nelson.

"Oh, and here's a carton of cigarettes," he said, pulling the box from inside his jacket. "I was meaning to give you these. I don't smoke, and a friend gave them to me."

"I don't smoke, either," said Nelson.

"Well, you can throw them out," said Steph. "If you don't want to throw them out, take them down to the bar and sell them."

Steph gave Jennifer a hug and was out the door.

"I'll be in touch," he said.

Later that evening, as Jennifer and Nelson were getting ready for bed, Nelson was pleased with himself. "A hundred and fifty dollars is not bad for a couple days' work," he said. But Jennifer wasn't so sure.

"I don't know, Nelson, something just doesn't feel right."

68

Jennifer's suspicion didn't let up. But Nelson had his own plan. Steph had offered Nelson a finder's fee of $500 if he could find his sister. On February 16, Steph had left Nelson a message saying that he had found the missing sister, and he wanted to meet at the Mount Peyton Hotel the next day.

But that morning Nelson was acting nervous.

"Well, I think it's weird that he wants to meet you up at the hotel," said Jennifer. "Why don't we drive around town to see if we can find him?"

They drove around for a while, then decided to drop by the local police station.

"That's the truck," said Jennifer, pointing to the big black pickup sitting in front of the station. "I know that's his licence plate."

Suddenly Nelson got scared, and he and Jennifer headed straight to Gander to see his mother.

Jennifer was the first to call the police, and then his mother called.

"We want to know if this is illegal, or if someone is trying to get Nelson in trouble."

The RCMP officer assured them there was nothing illegal about helping someone find his missing sister, and that was the end of the conversation.

That evening, they headed back to Grand Falls–Windsor. There was a note on the door. It was from Steph, asking them to call.

"That wasn't my truck," Steph reassured them. "You know, Nelson, if you don't show up for work—that isn't good for business."

Jennifer knew it had in fact been his truck they saw at the police station, but she said nothing.

"I have a job for you if you're interested," said Steph. "I need someone to drive a truck to Corner Brook for me."

Nelson jumped at the chance, agreeing he would be ready the next morning.

69

February 17, 2005.

Nelson and Jennifer were up early to get ready for the trip to Corner Brook. Nelson was eager to make the trip, and he had made it clear he was hoping to get plenty more jobs.

Since they had been in the apartment for only a couple of days, they still didn't have the phone hooked up. So far they had relied on their neighbours, who didn't seem to mind them popping by to make calls.

On this morning, Jennifer wanted to make sure she arranged to have the phone hooked up before they left for the day.

She went next door and called the telephone company. Fortunately, it didn't look like it would take long before they could carry out the installation.

"Thanks for letting me use your phone," Jennifer told her neighbours as she headed out the door. "They'll be here to hook up our phone in the next couple days, so at least we won't have to be bothering you guys all the time."

As Jennifer was leaving her neighbours' house, she could hear yelling coming from her apartment.

There was no mistaking the thick French accent of Steph. And she knew he was mad. To be perfectly honest, she wasn't sure she was willing to deal with an angry Steph. His behaviour had already made her nervous. In fact, there were times she thought he was a complete lunatic with the way he was overly affectionate toward her.

"I can't work like this," yelled Steph. "You can't go bringing your wife to work!"

Jennifer watched as Steph jumped in the truck. He grabbed the attention of the neighbourhood when he squealed the tires leaving the driveway.

"He says you can't come," said Nelson.

Nelson and Jennifer went back into the apartment. She could see Nelson was frustrated. He wanted the job, but he didn't want to go alone. But after only about thirty minutes, Steph was back.

"Okay, you can bring your wife," said Steph. "But you won't be allowed to do this if you're going to be working for me all the time."

"How much will I get paid?" asked Nelson.

"You don't need to ask that kind of stuff," said Steph.

Nelson and Steph left in the pickup and, shortly after, Nelson arrived back at the apartment in a large van. All Jennifer could think about as she stepped into the van was what kind of mood Nelson would be in for the next four hours of the trip. She was sure there would be some kind of episode.

Instead, the ride was mostly uneventful.

When they arrived in Corner Brook, Steph was there along with another man. Nelson and the two men were looking in the back of the trailer, where Jennifer had learned they were carrying a new snowmobile that was being delivered to Cox's Cove.

"You and Nelson will drive back with me," said Steph after he knocked on Jennifer's window.

She and Nelson climbed into the black pickup, and they headed for home.

Jennifer listened as Nelson told Steph how much he enjoyed driving and how he was willing to do more jobs. During the drive, Steph received a phone call from someone who needed something driven to Nova Scotia.

As soon as Steph hung up, Nelson offered to make the trip.

Back in Grand Falls, Jennifer got out of the truck and went inside. Nelson and Steph had a brief conversation in the truck, and Nelson was paid $220.

70

February 18, 2005.

There was a knock at the door. Jennifer looked over at the clock to realize it was nearly nine o'clock. She wondered who it could be, but when she opened the door, she saw Steph.

"Nelson's not home," she said. "He's gone to pick up something to eat, but Nelson told me that you should wait for him if you were to show up."

Steph sat down at the table, and Nelson was there in only five minutes.

"Hey, Steph," said Nelson, taking off his shoes. "I was hoping to hear from you. Do you have any work?

"I do," said Steph. "Tomorrow there will be a van waiting for you down at the mill around lunchtime. I want you to pick it up and drive into St. John's. Once you get in there, call me."

Steph handed Nelson $100 for gas money and left.

71

February 19, 2005.

Nelson showed up at the apartment to pick up Jennifer in the U-Haul, even though he hadn't discussed taking her with Steph. Jennifer was worried about what kind of business Steph was into, and Nelson was suspicious as well. So they agreed she would go.

When she opened the door to the truck, she was far from prepared for the condition of the vehicle. The entire dashboard appeared to be falling out on the floor.

She closed the door and put on her seat belt, only to discover that the door really hadn't closed at all.

Holding the door while Nelson drove, she said, "My God, I can't drive to St. John's like this!"

Jennifer opened the glovebox and found a small piece of rope. It was just enough to tie the door to the bottom of the seat. Although it seemed like it would hold, she knew this would be a long and anxious trip.

No sooner did she have the door fixed when she looked over to see that there was no rear-view mirror on Nelson's side of the truck.

"What kind of vehicle is this supposed to be?" she said.

Two hours later and the door appeared to be holding up. But suddenly, Nelson began to act strangely.

"What's wrong?" she said. But she already knew.

Nelson had begun patting his stomach. "What, what, what," he repeated.

It was a seizure.

For a moment Jennifer thought they were going to be killed, but she reacted quickly by reaching her leg over and putting it underneath his. She slowly lifted his leg off the gas and applied the brakes, all while steering the truck safely to the shoulder of the highway.

"What, what," Nelson continued. Jennifer allowed the seizure to run its course for the next fifteen minutes or so.

"What happened?" he asked.

"You had a seizure," she told him. "Just rest for a few minutes, Nelson. You aren't driving anywhere in your condition."

For the next ten minutes or so, Nelson asked several times where they were, and where they were going. Finally, after sitting on the highway for nearly half an hour, he came to his senses.

They got back on the highway and continued on to St. John's. Once there, they booked into their room at the

Holiday Inn. Steph was going to be there at 6:30 p.m., and he wasn't even aware that Jennifer was with Nelson.

When he knocked on the hotel room door at 6:10, Jennifer went into the washroom. Nelson wanted her to listen to what Steph was saying in order to find out whether what he was doing was illegal. Or if someone was just out get him.

"We need to meet our client downtown," said Steph. "Get ready, we're going to get something to eat."

Jennifer listened as Nelson tried to get out of having to go downtown, but she could hear Steph putting the pressure on as well.

"You are acting weird, Nelson," she heard Steph say. "I'm starting to wonder if I should keep you on or not."

Finally, she heard Nelson confess that Jennifer was also in the room. After a moment, she flushed the toilet and walked out into the room.

Eventually, Steph convinced Nelson they had to meet with the client if he was to do any more business. Jennifer was left in the room to wait.

Nelson came back a couple of hours later. Alone.

"What was so important?" Jennifer asked.

"I don't know," said Nelson. She could see he was scared. Nelson went on to tell her that they were driving so fast he thought they were going to flip over. "I thought they were going to throw me in the harbour," he said.

Jennifer decided not to ask anything more.

But on the trip back to Grand Falls, Jennifer couldn't resist.

"Are you legit or what?" Jennifer asked Steph. "Are you dealing drugs? 'Cause if you are, Nelson's not having no part of it."

"I'm not a pig or anything like that," said Steph. "When I get used to you, I'll tell you about my past. I've done things in my past, and when I get to know you better, I'll tell you."

Nelson said he was relieved, and the two of them went on to talk about how important it was to be honest, loyal, and truthful in order to have a good working relationship. Steph also told him about another man he did business with, named Pat.

He hoped Nelson would be able to help Pat out, while Steph returned to the mainland.

Back in Grand Falls, Nelson was paid $300. Once again, Jennifer didn't see the transaction.

72

February 22, 2005.

Nelson and Steph flew to Halifax. They rented a vehicle at the airport and, as they drove into town, Steph explained to Nelson that he had done a lot of bad shit in his life. Nelson told him that he had done some bad things, too, and once they got to know each other, he'd tell Steph about it. That night he was introduced to Pat, who Nelson believed was the company's Maritimes manager. After a few days of driving and delivering what he believed to be airplane parts, Nelson was instructed to deliver freight back onto the island and on to St. John's. On February 28 in St. John's, he was paid $1,100 for this work.

73

Jennifer wasn't sure what to think when she met Pat for the first time. Apparently, Nelson hadn't bothered to tell him that she was making the trip into St. John's with him, but Pat didn't seem to be the type to get as upset as Steph.

Once they had checked out of the hotel, she and Nelson climbed into the truck with Pat and started the trip back to Grand Falls–Windsor.

Jennifer sat in the back, and she had the feeling that Nelson and Pat were probably avoiding talking about work because she was there. She knew Nelson didn't want her to be talking, so she kept quiet for nearly the entire trip.

Nelson spent most of his time talking about the province and how well he knew the roads around the island.

They stopped at the Tim Hortons in Clarenville along the way, and they made another stop for pizza in Gander.

By the time they made it back to their home, Jennifer had started to take a liking to Pat. At least he wasn't hugging her all the time like Steph, and he was a lot easier to understand. Even though the French accent was still there.

Pat dropped them off at the apartment, but it wasn't long before Nelson started to get anxious again. He liked his work. He liked the money and wanted to get back on the road.

And although his moods were a lot better, Jennifer was enjoying the peace of having him away.

74

March 3, 2005.

Nelson was tasked with delivering a truck to St. John's, where Pat would be waiting. Over dinner, Pat told Nelson there were two things he hated in life. The first being the police, or pigs, as he put it. If they knew he was on the island, they would be all over him. Pat also made it clear he hated anyone who was pretending to be righteous in a criminal organization.

"If you rat on me, you are taking a one-way street."

Pat also stressed that people who work in the organization didn't tell stories to their wives.

Nelson said he wanted to take Jennifer to either Florida or Hawaii. And Pat said if he kept working hard, he'd soon be able to afford it.

The next morning they delivered another quad across the island to Deer Lake.

75

Jennifer was exhausted. They had just made the return trip from St. John's. Nelson and Pat were still out in the truck. She assumed Nelson was being paid, although she hadn't ever actually seen him getting paid for his work.

But she knew he was making good money. Nelson's mood had been oddly calm these past few weeks. It was obvious that he respected Steph and Pat, and he wanted to be like them.

And he also loved the work. She couldn't ever remember him being as content as he was driving around in his new job.

In the days between jobs, he was on the edge of his seat waiting for the next phone call from Pat.

A couple days after they returned from their most recent trip, he couldn't wait any longer.

First thing on the morning of March 15, he called Pat.

This time there was a job. Jennifer listened to Nelson's phone conversation with Pat.

"Well, I've got a dentist appointment on Wednesday," Nelson told Pat. Nelson didn't want to say yes right away. He was buying time so he could talk it over with Jennifer.

"He wants me to drive to St. John's, but they might need me for the rest of the week," Nelson told her. "I might have to go out of the province."

After some discussion, Nelson decided he would take the job.

"Will three pairs of jeans be enough?" Jennifer yelled out as she packed his overnight bag.

She still wondered about the company, but the thought of having Nelson away for the next week was appealing.

As soon as he was packed, Nelson took the car and headed for Gander. She knew that he was probably going to be flying to Halifax, but Nelson didn't say anything about what his business would be there.

Her only regret was that he didn't leave her the car so she could pick up some groceries at the food bank. But then, she wasn't able to drive the standard transmission, anyway.

76

March 16, 2005.

Nelson flew to Halifax, and for the next few days he would have a full schedule.

His first job was to pick up a package containing fraudulent credit cards at the YMCA. After a night at the casino, he and Pat had to drive from Halifax to Fredericton. On March 18, they drove back to Halifax, and Nelson was paid for the week's work. He was then told he would fly back to Newfoundland.

But first he let Pat know how much he was enjoying his friendship. He also liked working on the mainland. He knew the money was good, and Jennifer didn't mind.

After a few days at home, Nelson was back on another flight to Halifax, on March 21. He and Pat drove to Fredericton, had dinner, and stayed at a hotel. The next day, they drove to Woodstock on the United States border. There they met with a man who gave Nelson a bag. Nelson was to take the bag, buy a bus ticket, and head back to Moncton.

Nelson was nervous the police might have been watching him, but he assured Pat he didn't mind doing this kind of work as long as the money was good.

He was paid $500 and sent back to Gander.

A couple of weeks later, Pat picked Nelson up at the airport in Halifax once again. The next day, he had the job of delivering a package to Truro, and then he had to take a train to Montreal.

That night he stayed at the hotel next to the casino and was given $450 for his expenses and another $50 to cover the cost of interest on his credit card.

The next day, in Truro, Nelson was told he was going

to need some nice clothing for Montreal. Pat bought him a shirt, pants, some socks, and even a new pair of shoes. They drove back to Halifax, where Nelson was given a package and Pat paid another man $25,000 in cash. Steph was there, too. Nelson counted the money, and listened. Pat told the man, if he ever told anyone where the package came from, he would have to learn to swim real fast. They made it clear to Nelson that as long as a guy doesn't have any limitations, there were bigger jobs. Bigger pay.

Nelson told them he had no limitations.

But Steph also told him how he felt about rats. Rats should go in the water.

Steph and Pat said they were a circle—family. And when you're in the circle, the money gets better. But Nelson was told he wasn't part of the circle. That was up to the boss.

The next day, April 9, Nelson left for Montreal on the train with the task of delivering another package. This time it was a suitcase, and Pat agreed to meet him there. That night Nelson went to a steak house downtown with Steph, Pat, and their girlfriends. Nelson and Pat's girlfriend, Carol, hit it off immediately. It was a great social night with a lot of laughs. In fact, Nelson even had a couple of glasses of wine and made a toast to the boss, someone he hadn't met. It was the first time Pat had seen him drink. But then, they were having a great time, and Nelson couldn't wait to introduce Jennifer to Carol.

77

April 11, 2005.

Nelson and Steph had lunch alone. Nelson learned the structure of the organization he was working for and learned there would be more risk if he wanted to move up the ladder. Steph also explained the organization controlled seventy per cent of the prostitution in Montreal and took a percentage from all the money earned.

According to Steph, "I told Mr. Hart that I had to deal with those two prostitutes and, as a result, they couldn't earn money for a while. I had assaulted them. I had to send a message to them so that we didn't get ripped off."

Nelson told Steph he had no problem getting his hands dirty, either, and that he had done something terrible in his past. He explained one day he would tell them, and it would bring tears to Steph's eyes.

Steph, too, said he had terrible skeletons in his closet, and he liked the fact Nelson was being honest.

Nelson said he had dealt with two people and they were both in the ground now. He said it was all over the news and everyone talked about it.

Steph told Nelson he didn't have to say things to impress him.

But Nelson said he could prove it. Everyone had talked about it, and there were 600 people in the church. He took out his wallet, opened it, and there was a picture of two little girls wearing red dresses. Nelson showed him the pictures and said he'd leave it at that.

Steph pressed him.

Nelson said the girls in the picture were his daughters. He went on to say the police were talking to him and he didn't tell them anything about what he'd done. He told Steph one murder was twenty-five years, but he was looking at fifty years because he did two murders. He said he got away with it because of family. He said that when he got rid of his kids, he had planned it. When the cops tried to get him, he kept his mouth shut, and now there was no heat on him.

He told Steph they were blood brothers now.

After lunch, Pat picked up Nelson and they drove to Cornwall, Ontario. When they arrived, they picked up a truck loaded with a large quantity of cigarettes and brought it to a warehouse back in Montreal. After they unloaded the truck, they went to dinner.

For Nelson, the expensive restaurants were something he had never experienced. He told Pat there were times he didn't feel comfortable because it was all so new.

But he liked this new life, and he didn't want to go back to work in Newfoundland. Instead, he wanted Jennifer on the mainland with him.

78

April 12, 2005.

Nelson's job was to transport a package from Montreal to Ottawa. Steph met him at an Ottawa hotel, where they waited for the buyer of the package Nelson had delivered.

They sent him to several locations before telling the buyer their real location.

Once he arrived, they got down to business. He brought a bag filled with money. Fifty thousand dollars in US dollars, to be exact. Nelson counted it while the other

The actual book undercover operators used to hide the fake passports. Nelson thought they were selling them for $50,000 US in an Ottawa hotel room.

men talked about their investments in New York and Chicago.

Steph told Nelson to go into the washroom and retrieve the bag he had brought from Montreal. Inside was a book that had sections cut out. Inside the cavities were fake passports that the buyer was assured were of top quality.

But the buyer was more interested in talking about the organization and his connections. Bragging.

He was sitting on the couch when Steph walked over and slapped him across the face. He had no business talking about Steph's business.

With the $50,000 in his pocket, Steph and Nelson headed to a pub for something to eat.

79

"I don't have anything to wear," Jennifer said.

Nelson had just finished telling her that she was going to Halifax.

For the past few weeks, life had been relatively peaceful for Jennifer. Nelson was a changed man. He hadn't been violent toward her once. In fact, his behaviour had changed so much for the better, she was looking forward to the trip to Halifax.

"Well, at least you've got the new clothes they bought you," she said. "I don't really feel comfortable going there with these old rags."

But Nelson had recently bought her a new coat while he was in New Brunswick, and he told her she would look fine.

"I think you'll really like Carol," he told her.

She knew the money for new clothes wouldn't come, so she gave up asking. Instead, she packed her two best pairs of jeans and a couple of decent shirts. She thanked God they wouldn't see how badly she was in need of new underwear. And while her boots were far from adequate, at least they covered up the holes in her socks.

Jennifer couldn't believe that Nelson had landed a job that required social trips to other provinces, but here they were—on a flight to Nova Scotia.

As soon as they got off the plane, Pat was there to meet them. She could instantly see that he and Nelson had become very close over the past few weeks. And to be honest, she liked Pat as well.

"Where's Carol?" asked Nelson. "I was hoping she would be here."

"Oh, she's still getting ready," Pat replied. "It takes her forever."

They drove through Halifax, and from the back seat Jennifer could see the tall buildings downtown. Pat pulled up in front of the glass hotel doors and came around to help her with her bags.

Inside the lobby, Jennifer waited uncomfortably as Nelson and Pat had a quick conversation. She felt like she was now in Nelson's new life, and she waited for direction from him. Everything was new and fancy. Even Nelson had become higher-class in her eyes.

Finally, Nelson walked over to where she stood with the bags.

"Pat is going to be back to pick us up in a minute," he said. "Let's go up to our room to get ready for dinner."

In their room, Jennifer became even more self-conscious of what she was wearing. She longed for a new outfit so she could feel part of this environment. She looked out the window overlooking the city. Part of her was excited to be going out to dinner, but she felt nervous and inadequate at the same time.

"Let's go downstairs to the casino," Nelson told Jennifer.

She wasn't aware that there was a casino in the building, but she wasn't surprised that was where Nelson wanted to go.

Inside, she was in awe of the sheer size of the room, and the noise. The bells and games rang in her ears.

"I need to go find a washroom," Jennifer told Nelson.

Nelson pointed her to the washroom, and inside she drew a deep breath. Looking at herself in the largest mirror Jennifer had ever seen, she felt better just to be away from the noise and the people. She looked at the women standing next to her. They were wearing dresses and were glittering in jewellery. She had never felt so poor or so unattractive in her life.

When she regained her composure, Jennifer went back outside. She looked around the room and realized Nelson was nowhere to be seen. What would she do? There was no way she could ever find him here. She didn't know where to look, and she didn't want to.

But she had no choice but to find him. Slowly she began to focus and stepped down onto the main floor. She delicately walked through the crowd and passed the beautifully dressed people until she saw Nelson sitting at a table. He already had a pile of chips in front of him, but Jennifer didn't care. She was just relieved not to be alone here.

For a moment Jennifer had been worried the old Nelson was back, and that he had abandoned her here in another province.

"There you are," he said. "Pat just called, and we have to meet him out in the lobby."

Jennifer's heart began to pound again. She was nervous that Carol wouldn't like her. Especially the way she was dressed.

Pat was waiting in the lobby, but again there was no sign of Carol.

"Come on," he waved.

As they walked through the big glass doors, Jennifer could see Carol in the truck.

Outside, the fresh saltwater air was just what Jennifer needed. Once they were in the truck, Nelson and Pat did the introductions.

"How about we drop you girls off at the doors, and we'll go park the truck," said Pat. "Will that be okay?"

The girls agreed and got out near the front entrance of The Keg. Several times over the past few weeks, Jennifer had heard Nelson say they had eaten here while on business. She now realized first-hand the kind of lifestyle he had been living, while she had been at home eating from food hampers from the local food bank.

Even the restaurant doors looked elegant.

But among the nicely dressed couples and groups, she noticed something odd.

"Carol," she said. "Why are those girls sitting on the grass over there?"

"They're prostitutes," said Pat.

Jennifer was stunned. It was the first time in her life she had ever seen prostitutes. Again she felt overwhelmed.

Inside the restaurant, they waited for Nelson and Pat. Jennifer watched Nelson as he walked toward the building. He was confident. She could see he was also very excited about tonight. Part of her felt like she hardly knew this man compared to the old Nelson.

He even held the chair for her to sit down. As she looked around, she felt like even the waitresses were dressed better than her. It was uncomfortable, and she was worried she might make Nelson angry by being so out of place.

Jennifer was relieved when the server filled her glass with water. She thought her throat was about to close off. Then she looked at the menu. The prices were staggering, and she had never tried any of the dishes written before her.

It was as if Nelson knew exactly what she was thinking. He grabbed the menu and started looking through. He then placed the menu in front of him, and when the server took their order, Nelson ordered for her. She trusted he knew what she liked and would order something good.

Meanwhile, Pat had ordered a bottle of wine, which was placed in the middle of the table.

"Let's celebrate our friendship," he said as he grabbed the bottle.

"I'm not drinking tonight," said Nelson. "Jennifer doesn't drink, either."

"Oh well," laughed Pat. He shook the bottle and popped the cork.

Jennifer was shocked to see the champagne cork strike the high ceiling of the restaurant. The golden liquid turned into a fountain that poured into the air and all over the floor.

She noticed that Nelson and Pat didn't talk about work all evening. They made small talk, and Carol was asking Jennifer a lot of questions about herself. Gradually she began to feel very comfortable with Carol. And the food was perhaps the best she had ever tasted.

At the end of the evening, the server put the bill on the table. But Nelson, Pat, and Carol continued to laugh and talk.

Jennifer could see some of the print on that bill. Specifically, the $200 bottle of wine she had just seen spill over the floor.

80

Jennifer was enjoying the warmth of the shower as she went over the events of the night before in her mind. She still found it difficult to believe she was here. She found it difficult to believe that this was Nelson's job.

She shut off the shower, knowing that Pat and Carol would soon be there. They were having breakfast at the casino this morning.

When she walked out into the room, Nelson was already dressed. She looked through her suitcase, wishing she had something a little newer to wear. She glanced over at Nelson in his new clothes, and she knew there was no point in asking.

They headed downstairs to meet Pat and Carol.

"Good morning," said Pat. "I was hoping we could eat at the casino, but it's still closed."

Jennifer glanced at the clock on the lobby wall and realized it was still only ten thirty in the morning.

"Let's head across the road to the Delta," said Pat.

At the restaurant, the four of them sat down and ate breakfast. Nelson and Pat were anxious to get going. While he didn't say where, Jennifer knew they had business to take care of that required a drive.

Meanwhile, Carol wanted to go shopping.

"Here's $200," said Pat. "You girls head over to the Mic Mac Mall and have some fun."

Shopping sounded like fun, but with no money in her pocket, it didn't hold much appeal.

Nelson watched as Pat passed the money over to Carol.

Unexpectedly, Jennifer watched as Nelson pulled his wallet from his pocket.

Was he going to give her money?

Sure enough, he pulled a crisp $100 bill from the wallet and passed it across the table. Then he went on to offer to pay for breakfast for the four of them.

Jennifer was stunned, but she gladly accepted the money. Suddenly, she was very excited about the shopping trip. Carol needed to go to the washroom while they waited for the cab. Nelson pulled her aside.

"I gave you the money because Pat gave some to Carol," he whispered. "But don't spend one cent of it."

She wasn't surprised. By the time Carol came out of the washroom, the taxi was already there. Jennifer hopped in and they drove to the mall.

She had never seen a mall quite like it. And Carol seemed right at home as she flicked through the racks and found some great deals.

"Why haven't you bought anything?" Carol asked.

"I don't know, I just haven't found anything I really liked yet," Jennifer replied.

She left the mall without breaking the $100, but she refused to let Carol pay for the cab both ways. The fare was over $20.

So when they got back to the hotel, Jennifer paid for the cab, knowing Nelson wasn't going to like it one bit.

Alone, she went up to the hotel room and watched some television. A couple hours later, Nelson returned to the room. He barely had the door shut when he asked, "Where's my money?"

Jennifer passed him the bills and loose change, and it was clear Nelson wasn't happy. She was expecting that Nelson wouldn't let up once he found out she'd spent the money. But he let it go much quicker than usual. However, there was no mistaking, he was still mad.

That evening they caught the flight back home.

But Jennifer wouldn't have to put up with Nelson being around for very long. In just a couple days, he boarded the flight back to Halifax and didn't come home until May 7.

81

May 11, 2005.

Nelson was needed back in Halifax. The next day, he caught the first flight out. The next morning he was assigned to pick up a package and fly to Montreal.

Once in Montreal, he had dinner at the Baton Rouge with Pat, Steph, and their girlfriends. The group left for the casino. There, Pat, Nelson, Steph, and a casino employee had a conversation about counterfeit casino chips. It was a good way to make money, and there was even a discussion that perhaps Nelson could go to Las Vegas to deal with "that kind of thing." Everyone was excited when they left that night.

The next night, Steph picked Nelson up at his hotel. He explained that a member of the organization had been caught driving drunk and his car had been seized by the police. Nelson agreed to help break into the impound to retrieve something from the car.

At 1:30 a.m., May 14, Nelson put on a pair of gloves and a balaclava. With a bag and a set of bolt cutters, he busted the lock and entered the compound. When they tried to break the window, a car alarm went off, so Nelson and Steph grabbed a bag from the under the seat and ran out. The bag contained $30,000 in cash.

82

Jennifer could hardly believe what she was hearing.

"Let's go out to Norris Arm so you can pick out the headstone," Nelson told her.

Until now, she had to fight to be able to go visit the graves, and here was Nelson willing to spend hundreds of dollars to buy the headstones. Finally. She'd been longing to find a permanent marker for the gravesites, and now she would finally get the chance.

She was starting to like the new Nelson more all the time.

The two of them went inside and Jennifer picked out the one she liked best. She picked out the pictures and the verse that would be engraved on the front.

When she was finished, Nelson took his wallet and made the down payment.

"I'll pay the rest when it gets here," he said. "Don't worry, I have the money."

83

May 16, 2005.

Nelson had taken a flight to Vancouver. Steph picked him up at the airport, and once they had booked into the hotel, the two hit the casino.

"There's a big job coming up, and I need eight guys," Steph told him. "Every guy is looking for $20,000 to $25,000. Are you interested?"

Nelson was very interested, but first Nelson would have to be authorized by the boss.

The next day, Nelson and Steph drove to a warehouse in Port Coquitlam, where they met a man who Nelson believed was a member of the Hells Angels. He gave Steph money in exchange for the suitcase Nelson had brought from Montreal. They stopped and counted the money—$20,000.

Nelson told Steph that he was getting anxious to convince Jennifer they should move to the mainland. That's where the work was, and that's where he could make the most money.

The following day, Steph picked Nelson up at his hotel. They were delivering a package across town when Steph got an urgent phone call telling him to meet with the boss. They turned around and headed toward the Vancouver Yacht Club.

On board the boat, they had a glass of wine until the boss arrived. His name was Al.

Steph introduced Nelson to Al as "his Newfie buddy," and then Nelson was escorted outside so Steph and Al could talk privately.

"I asked whether you could be involved in the big job," Steph told Nelson. "But he wants to check you out first to make sure you're not a rat and to make sure you won't cause any problems."

Nelson continued on with his work for the day. He picked up a package from a locker and then took the bus to Chilliwack—about an hour and a half by bus. In Chilliwack, Steph picked him up and they drove back to Vancouver.

"If I could get this job I would be set," Nelson told Steph. "Do you know how poor I am?"

Nelson told Steph about having to use the food banks, and having to decide whether he would eat or pay the heat bill. He told him how they had no bed and that they slept on the floor. They were so poor, there were times when Jennifer used plastic bags and old rags to make tampons and pads for her period.

"I don't want to go back to that," Nelson told him.

"What would you do if Jennifer says you are travelling too much?" asked Steph.

Nelson told him that if there was a choice, he would leave her.

The next day Nelson was at the airport, ready to return to Newfoundland.

He was paid $4,000.

84

It seemed like months since Nelson and Jennifer had spent any time together. And today, as she watched his car pull into the driveway, she was looking forward to seeing him.

She wondered what he'd been up to since he was home last. She knew he'd had dinner with Carol and Pat in Montreal. Carol now called her on a daily basis. Just about every night the phone would ring, and it would be Carol. She always wanted to know how Jennifer was feeling, and she was extremely concerned with what Jennifer had to eat each day.

Jennifer always lied and said she had plenty of food, but the truth was the cupboards were usually bare. She relied on the food bank, when she could get there. They did own a car, but it was a manual transmission, so Jennifer couldn't drive anywhere.

When things got really desperate, she would phone Nelson and beg him for money. Over time she learned that he would leave $20 bills hidden around the house. If he felt she needed money badly enough, he would give up the location of the money.

But he always seemed to be in a good mood these days, and today was no different. He came into the house, and Jennifer started unpacking his bags.

"What do you want for supper?" she asked him. "There's not much here, so you're going to have to give me a ride down to the food bank so I can pick up some stuff."

But Nelson wasn't interested in supper. He wanted to go out for a while.

As soon as they left the house, Nelson drove straight to S&S Auto. He was buying a new car.

"Well, you need a car to drive while I'm on the mainland at work," he told her. "This standard is no good to you, so we'll buy an automatic."

Jennifer was excited. They took several cars out for a test drive, and he finally settled on a Pontiac Sunfire that was nearly brand new and cost $10,000.

Nelson was riding high in his new lifestyle. The next day, when he came home, he had a small box.

"Come and have a look," he told Jennifer.

Inside was a stack of business cards. It read "B.C.W. Transport, Coast to Coast Service" with the phone number and address of the company.

But they didn't have long before Nelson was called back to work on the mainland.

Before he left, he told her to use the car only if she really needed to. He wrote down the kilometres on the car before he left, with one rule. If he felt she was driving it more than she needed to, he would take the keys.

85

May 25, 2005.

Nelson was on the flight from Gander back to Halifax. There he was given a package and instructed to transport it to Montreal by train.

The next day, Steph, Nelson, and Pat met at a stripper bar. They had a VIP room in the back with a table. There they discussed business on a U-shaped sofa. Steph said he and Pat were going to Vegas this weekend, but Nelson couldn't go. He hadn't gotten the green light from the boss.

Nelson was to catch a flight back to Newfoundland in the morning, and he was disappointed to be left out.

86

"We're going to get a chance to spend some time with Pat and Carol again," Nelson announced.

He had just gotten off the phone. Jennifer was cleaning the apartment.

"When?"

"Tomorrow," Nelson replied. "We're going to drive into St. John's, and they'll meet us there."

Nelson and Jennifer were on their way travelling east, first thing in the morning. Four hours later, they arrived in the city and checked into their hotel room. Jennifer decided to get a shower because they were going out to dinner, and from her previous experience she knew it would be somewhere nice.

By the time she got dressed, Pat and Carol were waiting downstairs.

She had to admit, it was nice to see Carol again. In some ways, Jennifer felt like they were indeed becoming friends. The four of them headed up over Signal Hill toward the Battery Hotel. That's where they'd be having dinner tonight, and she could see Nelson was excited for them all to be together again.

For the first part of the evening, Nelson couldn't wait to tell Pat and Carol all about the car they had bought. How it was in great condition, and how Jennifer now had a car to drive while he was away at work.

"You know, we should plan a trip together, the four of us, for the summer," said Pat.

Suddenly, everyone was tossing around ideas.

"Me and Carol will find the biggest RV around to rent, and we could pick you guys up in Grand Falls," Pat suggested. "Maybe we could go to the Salmon Festival while we are there, then take the ferry to Halifax."

Everyone was so excited. Nelson wanted to get a video camera.

"We'll need a feed of lobsters along the way," Pat laughed.

Finally, dessert arrived, a bakeapple parfait. Jennifer explained to Pat what a bakeapple was, and that it wasn't a baked apple. Instead, it was a local Newfoundland berry.

To finish off the evening, they took a drive to the top of Signal Hill for a view of the city. But the high winds cut their sightseeing visit short.

Pat and Carol drove them back to their hotel, where Nelson was told he'd be flying to Halifax in the morning.

Jennifer had to take the bus back to Grand Falls.

87

June 3, 2005.

At the Toronto airport, Pat was there to pick up Nelson. From there they drove to a business where a man showed up with a briefcase. It contained $75,000, all of which was counted by Nelson. A short while later, another man showed up who worked for the company. Nelson counted $100,000 with the aid of a money counter. Later that day, another briefcase was delivered, again containing $100,000.

Nelson told Pat that he planned for him and Jennifer to move to the outskirts of Halifax. He talked about how excited he was to go on a trip this summer. He suggested maybe in the fall they could go to California.

The next day, Nelson and Pat spent time at the Woodbine

Racetrack. There Pat instructed him that the next day he would have to take a package to Ottawa. He overnighted in Ottawa and picked up a package that was to be transferred to Montreal. In Montreal, the next day, Steph picked him up at the bus depot.

"Do you want to go home?" Steph asked him on the way to the hotel.

Nelson didn't want to go home. He was enjoying the mainland. The next day, June 7, Steph and Nelson drove from Montreal to Cornwall.

Along the way they stopped at a pub across the river from the United States border. Steph was taking pictures with his digital camera, and he was also marking locations with a GPS.

It was all part of the information they would need for the big job, and Steph said he wanted Nelson to see the place just in case he was part of the action.

They returned to Montreal, and Nelson went to his hotel until ten o'clock that night. Steph picked him up, and they went to a pub with another member of the organization.

The next morning, Steph and Nelson drove out of town. They were going to see another town near the border. Again it was related to the big job coming up.

At around 11:30 a.m., Steph's phone rang. It was the boss.

Steph hung up and looked at Nelson. There were some issues that had come up when the boss checked him out. Nelson was not allowed to travel to the border that day.

"The boss did not tell me what the issue was because we were on the phone," Steph told Nelson.

Nelson was worried. He wasn't worried about the big job. Instead, his fear was that he wouldn't be able to hang out with Steph and Pat anymore. They were like his family.

They turned the car around and went back to the hotel.

88

Jennifer was nearly asleep when the phone rang. "Hello?"
For a moment the other end was silent, until finally Nelson spoke.
"How is everything back there?" he asked.
"Everything's all right," she said. "Why are you calling here so late?"
"I can't sleep. I have something I want to tell you."
Nelson went on to tell her the name of his hotel, and the room number. He also told her the police station was right across the road.
What left Jennifer puzzled for the rest of the night were his instructions. If anything was to happen to him, he wanted her to know where he was.
Nelson hung up, but it was a restless night for Jennifer. She wondered exactly what it was he was up to.

89

June 9, 2005.
The boss.
That morning, Steph and Nelson were on their way to another job when Steph got the call.
"The boss is in Montreal and he wants to see us."
Steph turned the car around and headed for the hotel. Inside, Al and his bodyguard were waiting in the lounge. The four of them went upstairs to the hotel room.
For the first while they talked about the Formula One races under way in Montreal, but it wasn't long before Al wanted to get down to business. He asked Steph and the bodyguard to leave.
The drapes were closed, and Nelson made himself comfortable on the couch.

The boss confronted Nelson about his past. In particular, he wanted to know about the allegation he had murdered his twin daughters. He told him there was a drug dealer who was offering up information to the police on the girls' deaths.

Nelson denied it.

Al continued to tell Nelson that he had to tell the truth so the organization could deal with it. Especially if he wanted to be involved in the "big job."

Nelson said he'd had a seizure that day and that he hadn't killed the girls.

But Al wasn't giving up. The organization didn't want the police snooping around.

Eventually, Nelson told him that he had killed the girls. He would rather they be dead than in the custody of his brother.

"I struck them with the shoulder, like that," Nelson said.

"This is just about the perfect murder," said Al.

"It was pretty well organized."

"You must be a thinker, eh?" asked Al.

"Sometimes it pays to be that way," said Nelson.

Two hours later, Nelson left the room, and he was excited. He was in. He was also put to work right away. The next day, he had to deliver a package to St. John's.

90

June 11, 2005.

So far Nelson had been paid a total of $15,000 for just four months' work, and now he could see the opportunity to make another $25,000 for just one job. And all he had to do was drive and deliver packages. For him it was a dream job.

In St. John's, Steph and another man showed up at his hotel first thing in the morning. Nelson was hardly awake when he finished counting $50,000 in cash.

Steph said Nelson would have to take the money to his house in Grand Falls, so the two of them were packed and on the highway in no time.

It was a long drive, and there was plenty to talk about.

At about the halfway point, they stopped in Clarenville for some lunch.

"My God, I can't believe he is willing to help me out with this situation with the girls," Nelson told Steph. He was extremely happy about his meeting with Al. He talked of how he regretted not having money when the girls were alive. He would have been able to afford a lawyer. That way he could have fought to make sure his brother didn't get custody of the girls, and he wouldn't have had to kill them.

Then there was the big job. Nelson was loving the idea of making $25,000. Steph told him he would get $12,500 up front, and he would get the other half once the job was competed.

And then there was the business of a drug dealer back in Gander who was telling the police that he had information for them regarding Nelson. He was claiming to have proof that it hadn't been an accident.

But Steph assured him, now that they were back in Newfoundland, he would be taken care of. When that job was done, he would call Nelson. Then Nelson would have to go to the local Walmart, where he could be captured on camera. That would provide his alibi.

But in the middle of their discussion, Steph got a phone call. A call from Al.

He wanted Steph to check out the scene at Little Harbour, where the girls had drowned.

Of course, it was right along the way.

So Nelson and Steph drove down the dirt road until Gander Lake came into view. There were docks and a few people hanging around.

"Al wants to know if it's possible someone was watching you that day," Steph said.

But Nelson assured him there was no one around. He was sure of it.

The boss wanted to see the layout of the area just in case someone saw it.

Once they arrived, both Nelson and Steph walked out toward the wharf where the girls had drowned.

"Let's go out and see some fishes, that's what I told them," Nelson said in his explanation of the events of August 4, 2002.

Steph crouched down on his knees, and Nelson showed him how he had bumped his daughters off the wharf.

91

Jennifer was kind of glad that Nelson was still in bed this morning. He had been gone for weeks, and even though his moods weren't nearly as bad, she could get more done without him in the way.

Last night he had picked up some groceries, and this morning she had plans for a big breakfast to celebrate.

While he was gone, there was very little food. She mostly relied on trips to the food bank or the occasional $20 bill she had to scavenge and beg for. But there wasn't any money for laundry, and today there was barely a clean piece of clothes in the house.

She found a couple of garbage bags and rounded up the clothes from around the bathroom. She would wait until Nelson got up before going into the bedroom and waking him up.

With the laundry ready to go, she pulled out the frying pan. Eggs, bologna, and toast. It was the perfect way to start what she hoped would be a good day. She had transportation again, not to mention food and a bit of extra money.

And if last night was any indication, she figured Nelson would probably be in a good mood this morning. It was becoming obvious that his trips were paying off big time.

With the sun shining through the kitchen window, she went about making breakfast. The aromas must have woken Nelson from his sleep, because it seemed like moments later he was sitting at the kitchen table.

She waited until he had his tea before pressing him about the things that needed to be done that day.

Once he started devouring the breakfast, she asked him, "Can we go to the laundromat today?"

Nelson didn't hesitate in telling her they would go, and Jennifer was relieved not to have to fight that particular battle. She believed part of the reason he was so agreeable these days was that he was spending less and less time in front of the slot machines. At least she had something to be thankful for.

Once breakfast was out of the way, they headed down to Union Street toward the laundromat. The back seat of the car was piled high with garbage bags containing nearly every piece of clothes they owned.

As she put Nelson's new clothes into the wash, she took extra care to make sure they didn't get damaged. She fastened the buttons and turned everything inside out before putting them into a delicate cycle. As she filled the washer and looked at his new clothes, she wondered just where he had been. Why had these people chosen him? It seemed like he was being treated exceptionally well for someone who was only used to driving around quads and skidoos.

With so much clothes it didn't take long before the first washer had completed its cycle, and Jennifer began the process of transferring everything to the dryers.

She had just moved the last load of sopping wet clothes to the dryer when Nelson's phone rang.

Even through the tiny speaker pinned to Nelson's ear,

she knew Steph's voice. Nelson was listening closely, his expression a mixture of fear and panic.

He hung up quickly. "We have to go now," he said.

"The clothes are still wet!" said Jennifer.

"I don't care, this is important, and I need you to do what I say."

They piled the clothes into the garbage bags, then stuffed them into the back seat of the Sunfire. Nelson pulled out of the parking lot in a hurry.

"We are going to Walmart," he said. "When we get there, I want you to stand next to me in front of the camera by the main doors. We are going to stand there for at least three minutes, and don't move."

Jennifer wondered if he was losing his mind. "Slow down!" she yelled. Nelson nearly ran a red light. As he swerved into the mall parking lot, he nearly struck another car.

Now Jennifer was getting really worried.

"Do you remember what I told you to do?" Nelson said.

"Why are we doing this?" she asked.

"Don't ask any questions, just do it," he said. Nelson took her by the hand and nearly ran to the front doors of Walmart. As soon as they stepped inside, he stopped dead in his tracks.

"Look up," he told Jennifer.

And she did. For the next three minutes, Nelson and Jennifer stood starting at the Walmart security camera.

92

Jennifer still couldn't understand what had happened, but Nelson was obviously under stress ever since the call from Steph at the laundromat.

He jumped when the phone rang suddenly.

"Hello," he said.

Jennifer could hear Steph's voice coming through on the cellphone's tiny speaker.

"I got to go to Gander," he said. "Give me your driver's licence. I've got to go to Gander Airport right away."

"Why do you need my licence? You don't need a licence to buy a plane ticket," Jennifer replied.

She instantly knew something was wrong. Suddenly, Jennifer had a very bad feeling about the way things were going down. Something was wrong.

Nelson left for the airport, and Jennifer figured she'd just go on and make supper like she'd planned.

She pulled out the frying pan and grabbed the salmon steaks out of the fridge. She'd been looking forward to the fish all day, but now her stomach was telling her that eating might not be the best idea. Yet she refused to give in. She heated up some oil on the stove and watched the pink meat as it sizzled in the pan.

She flipped over the first piece to see the golden crust, and suddenly her appetite returned with force.

But before she could turn over the next piece, there was a knock at the door.

It was the police.

"Jennifer Hart?" they asked.

"Yes."

"We need to tell you that Nelson is at the police station in Gander. We have arrested your husband for the murder of your two daughters."

Jennifer couldn't sit down, but she felt too light-headed to stand. She decided to just start walking around the apartment in circles. She tried to stop herself from throwing up, but it wasn't going to be easy.

She could hear Nelson's words: *I have something in the back of my mind that I'm going to take to my grave.*

For what seemed like an eternity, her world had suddenly become a dream that she was watching from afar.

It was the same feeling she experienced when she realized she wouldn't see her daughters again.

She watched helplessly as the officer walked into the apartment and turned off the stove for her. He then apologized for her loss, and the officers were on their way.

93

Jennifer could barely believe what was happening.

He had done it. Nelson had killed her girls. There were no more questions to be answered. The police had found out the truth.

She watched the familiar landmarks as the police officer drove toward the station in Grand Falls–Windsor.

How could he kill his own children? Jennifer had so many questions, but for now she chose to listen. She didn't know what to say anymore.

Suddenly, a familiar face appeared at the door of the tiny interview room at the police station. Jennifer remembered her name was Lori. She was from victim services.

"How are you doing?" she asked Jennifer. "Let's get ready. We're going to drive out to Gander. If you're feeling up to it, of course. That way you can get your car. It's at the detachment there."

During the hour-long drive to Gander, Jennifer didn't have much to say. Instead, the trip brought her through a range of emotions. She was hurt. The wounds from losing her daughters felt fresh once again. She had always questioned whether her husband could actually kill Karen and Krista, and now she had her answers.

She felt guilt. Why didn't she leave him when they were babies? She had always known there was something wrong with Nelson. Why hadn't she acted on those gut instincts long ago? Perhaps her children would be alive now.

And she was mad. How could he hate his own children so much he would drown them?

"Nelson confessed," Lori explained to her.

"What do you mean, confessed?" Jennifer asked.

"Jennifer, since the girls died three years ago, the RCMP have felt quite certain that Nelson's story didn't add up. You know they've suspected he killed the girls on purpose," Lori explained. "Well, four months ago they launched a sting operation called Mr. Big. You know Steph and Pat? Well, they're actually undercover operators. They had convinced Nelson he was working for an organization like the mob. He was recently offered a big job that offered to pay him a lot of money, but before he got the job, they asked him to come clean on what happened to the girls."

"What did he say?" Jennifer asked.

"He said he pushed the girls off the end of the wharf."

The conversation continued to play itself over and over in her mind as she went through the steps of retrieving the car from the police compound. Unsure of what to do, she drove to Nelson's mother's.

"He said he did it," Jennifer cried. "He told the police he planned it!"

"Calm down, Jennifer. You know Nelson was not capable of killing the girls. This is nothing but a set-up by the RCMP. They tricked him."

"But he said it!" Jennifer was sobbing uncontrollably. She felt like she had been sobbing ever since the girls had died.

"Jennifer, he didn't do it. You know it, and I know it. This was a set-up to get him to confess, and I'm not going to stop until the truth is told. We will get him out of jail. You know he didn't do it. They trapped him."

Nelson's mother showed strong determination when it came to her son's innocence. And the more Jennifer listened, the more she believed her mother-in-law.

Perhaps Nelson hadn't done it after all. Perhaps Nelson was innocent and it was the RCMP who deserved the blame.

With Nelson's mother, Jennifer felt like she still had some of her family left, and a little support. She stayed in Gander for a couple of days before heading back to Grand Falls. After two days, Nelson was transferred to the penitentiary in St. John's.

94

The tears streamed down her face as quickly as the rain beat off her windshield. Since the girls' deaths, driving past the sign reading "Little Harbour" had become nearly impossible without crying.

Today she longed for her girls even more as she drove back to Grand Falls–Windsor. Toward an empty apartment. A few years ago she had her own family, and today there was nothing. No husband, no children, and she didn't even know who to trust anymore.

As she struggled to keep the car on the road between the rivers of water on the pavement, she also struggled with her mind. Could the police have framed Nelson? But he had never really bonded with the girls, and she remembered how many times she felt as if Nelson didn't love them. He had even gone so far as to say he hated them.

It was all too much for her to comprehend. All she knew was that she had been through a lot in these past three years, and now she would have to relive it in a trial.

Jennifer opened the door to the apartment, and the smell of fish was the first thing to strike her. She had left in such a hurry, the fish she had started to cook was still sitting in the pan on the stove.

From a deep place, she summoned the energy to clean up the mess. Every move she made felt as though she were just acting out a dream. Like none of this could be real.

Finally, she sat at the kitchen table, and all she could hear was the rain beating at the windows. There was nothing she wanted to do, nothing she cared about anymore.

She grabbed a quick shower and decided a nap might be the only thing she was really in the mood for. Even though it was still the middle of the afternoon, she put on her nightshirt and crawled onto the mattress on the floor. *This is a good place*, she thought. And as she lay down, she silently wished that she could just stay here forever. She could see no point in ever getting up again.

She must have dozed off, because the sound of the phone ringing sounded like it was miles away. She didn't move as she continued to listen to the ringing. Whoever it was didn't matter.

But in the back of her mind she could hear their little voices. It was Karen and Krista urging her to get up.

She stood up and went out into the kitchen to answer the phone.

It was a collect call from the prison. Nelson.

"I only have a half-hour to talk," said Nelson. "But you and Mom have got to get me out of here!"

Jennifer could hear the panic in his voice as he told her about prison life. But there was also an urgency about what Jennifer was up to. He wanted to know where she had been, and whether or not she had cashed the welfare cheque.

He went on to tell her only to spend what she had to, and to send the rest to him.

The next day, Jennifer picked up a few groceries, set some money aside for gas, and sent the rest to the penitentiary.

95

Jennifer had just finished buying a new overnight bag for Nelson at the Bentley store. Then she had headed over to Walmart to do what Nelson wanted.

By the time Jennifer had finished the shopping trip, the overnight bag was full. There was everything from shaving cream to new jeans and T-shirts. She knew Nelson needed those things, but it left her with barely enough money to pay the rent.

And still Nelson had asked for more money. Money she didn't have.

The rent wasn't her only concern. Nelson was calling her collect every day. Some days he was calling two or three times to find out what she was doing. And there were other times he just wanted to talk about how badly he wanted to be out of the jail. But besides the emotional cost Jennifer was paying, she was also watching the phone bill climbing quickly. She knew the payments she was making to the phone company soon wouldn't be enough to offset the soaring costs.

Jennifer knew they were giving him a hard time. In one of his phone calls, he told her how he had been beaten up by the guards and left in isolation. His mother had gone so far as to call the prison to complain about the way Nelson was being treated. But even though he was spending a lot of his time in solitary confinement, Jennifer still had a hard time sympathizing with him. Despite supporting his mother outwardly, she had a nagging suspicion that it was possible Nelson was responsible for her losing the girls.

When he told her the guard had called him a baby killer, she wondered whether or not the guard was right.

96

With the trial set to begin in February, Jennifer began spending more time in Gander with Nelson's mother.

Each night she thought of the trial and the details that would come out. Nelson's mother, however, continued to reassure Jennifer that Nelson was indeed innocent. She believed he had been framed, and there was no way she was letting her son go to jail.

Together they did what they could for Nelson while he was in prison. Nelson's mother worked diligently to make sure he would be well represented in his trial. Derek Hogan, with the Legal Aid Commission, was chosen to represent him.

Nelson was constantly on the phone, and they were very busy times. Although there were occasions when Jennifer could barely keep up the goings-on, she was glad for the distraction.

In addition, spending more time in Gander meant she got to spend more time at the graveyard. Now that the girls had their headstone in place, Jennifer was busy making sure her daughters were remembered properly.

But no matter how busy she was, there were still times when she could only lie on their graves and cry. There were many times she only wished she could just dig them up and take them home.

Nelson was phoning every chance he got, which kept everyone busy. Each day there was a new story. Everyone was out to get him, or at least that's what he thought. Silently Jennifer wondered if he wasn't getting more and more agitated each time she talked to him.

But his mother wasn't about to give up, and finally she couldn't take it anymore. She wanted to go see Nelson at the prison.

So they packed up and headed for St. John's.

Jennifer had never been inside a prison before, and she thought it was the spookiest place she had ever seen. After they had entered a small room, they proceeded through a long tunnel, where they sat at a long table with the other visitors.

Before long, the guard brought Nelson out.

At first Jennifer thought he looked different somehow, but she soon realized he was the same old Nelson. Only now he needed her, and his mother, more than ever.

"You guys have got to get me out of here soon," he pleaded.

"It will only be a few weeks and the trial will begin," Jennifer reassured him. "If you're innocent, it won't be long and you will be out."

After their visit, his mother was more determined than ever to prove that Nelson was innocent.

Jennifer was there when his mother phoned the local television reporter. She wanted to tell Nelson's side of the story.

"The RCMP barbarized Nelson," she told him. "They followed him, they did everything in the world for three and a half years to try and get something on that man to prove that he drowned his two little girls. They came up empty because he's innocent.

"They turned on him and they set him up," she said. "They knew how poor he was at the time, they knew his circumstances. They knew he had a gambling problem. They knew right how to get to the core of Nelson, so they set him up and set him up good."

Jennifer and Nelson's mother were rarely apart these days as they prepared for the trial. Jennifer followed her and helped wherever she could. She was constantly making sure Nelson had what he needed in prison, and then there was also the question of securing a lawyer.

Of course, Nelson qualified for legal aid. However, an appointed lawyer wasn't going to be satisfactory for Nelson. Nelson would receive support to keep fighting until he got the lawyer of his choice.

97

As Jennifer sat in the courtroom, she again felt like the world around her had become a bad dream. Nelson's mother sat beside her, full of fury. This would be the trial that would prove her son's innocence, and she was there to make sure of it. It was also expected that his wife be there to support him.

Jennifer looked around the courtroom and saw some faces she knew, and others whom she didn't recognize. Suddenly, a door opened and two guards brought Nelson into the courtroom. There were chains around his feet, and a group of reporters rushed to the front of the courtroom. Through her tears, Jennifer heard the clicks of the cameras and saw the lights fixed on her husband.

If he wasn't a criminal, he sure looked like one to her at this moment.

He kept his head down as the cameras stayed focused on him.

First on the stand that day was a police officer who had been at Little Harbour that day in 2002.

As they went over the finest details of the scene at the lake, Jennifer realized that for the next few weeks she would have to relive everything that had happened.

Up next was a doctor who had examined Karen and Krista that morning. Most of the details were technical, and difficult to understand, but Jennifer was in agony as she listened to them talk about her girls.

98

It was Monday morning, the first day of week two of the trial. Jennifer got up and boiled the kettle. She didn't feel like getting dressed, and she was in no mood for driving back to Gander for another morning at the courtroom. But she knew Nelson's mother was counting on her. She was having trouble understanding much of what she had been listening to all week. It seemed the lawyer went on for hours about the most insignificant details.

Then there was his mother, who was constantly talking about Nelson. How hard a time he was going through, how unfairly he had been treated.

Even though Jennifer had her doubts, she still felt it was

her obligation to be there. Especially if her husband had been framed by those undercover RCMP.

Suddenly, there was a knock at the door, startling her. Who could it be so early in the morning?

"Can you come up to the house before you take off to Gander this morning?"

It was her landlord.

Jennifer went about the business of getting ready, making sure she had everything she had promised Nelson. There was a new shaver and some cream in the bag, though she could barely afford it these days. But she felt it was her job, as his wife, to do whatever she could to help.

She walked out of the apartment into the icy February morning. To the west she could see a storm moving in, but that wouldn't stop her from being in court.

Her landlords were waiting for her as soon as she knocked on their door. They'd been good to her, and she was curious why they wanted her this morning.

Harold held out an envelope.

"I want you to take this, and don't open it until you get to Gander," he said. "I take it you'll be going out to the court this morning. It must be hard on you. We've been watching the news all week."

"Yeah, it's all a bit confusing and tiring," she told him.

"Well, you take care of yourself and drive safely this morning," said Harold.

"Looks like we're going to have some weather."

Jennifer had no intention of waiting until she got to Gander to open the envelope. As soon as she finished gassing up the car, she pulled over to a side of the parking lot.

Inside the envelope was a $50 bill. Jennifer began to cry. She needed the help, but she didn't realize how obvious it was that she was suffering financially.

But there was something about that gift that made her feel stronger. Ready to endure the proceedings today. She knew there was a strong possibility that Mervin, Nelson's brother, would be there. At least there would be a friendly face in the courtroom.

Jennifer drove to Nelson's mother's and waited in the driveway. After a couple of minutes, Nelson's mother came out dressed in her beige leather jacket with a matching scarf. She looked sharp.

"Have a look at this," Jennifer shrieked, pulling the $50 bill from her pocket. "My landlord gave me this."

But Jennifer didn't think Nelson's mother shared in her excitement at all. Instead, she suggested Jennifer use the money to help Nelson out. However, this was one time Jennifer had no intention of passing the money over. She needed the money badly.

They made their way through the cold into the courthouse, and of course the cameras were there waiting. But Jennifer was gradually getting used to the cameras, though she still didn't like them.

Throughout the morning they continued to watch tapes of Nelson at the police station just hours after the girls had died. For three hours he was interviewed, and for the three hours he denied having hurt his children. Krista fell in the water and he left Karen with her. When he got back to Little Harbour, they were both in the lake. That was his story, and the police couldn't make him change it no matter how hard they tried.

Finally, Mervin walked up to the stand. Jennifer was instantly reminded of how much he cared for her and the girls.

The Crown attorney, Mark Linehan, made his way through a bunch of general questions, and Mervin explained that he was the middle child. Nelson was the oldest, and Stephen the youngest.

He asked him to point Nelson out in the courtroom.

Jennifer listened as he asked Mervin about how much contact he'd had with Jennifer and Nelson in the months prior to their deaths. He also asked about the day the girls died.

"Mr. Hart, what do you remember about the day of August 4, 2002?" asked Mr. Linehan.

"I was getting ready to go to Gander, to the derby and to see the kids," Mervin Hart told the court. "I was hoping to take them out to the demolition derby . . . and I got a call from Nels. He was trying to get a hold of Mom. Mom was in St. John's for that weekend. He was trying to get a number to her. He was upset, and he had to get a hold of her. Krista was out in Little Harbour. She was after falling into the water, and he was trying to get a hold of Mom."

Jennifer fought back the tears as she listened to her brother-in-law go over the details of having to identify Karen.

Then came the cross-examination by Derek Hogan, Nelson's lawyer.

"As Nelson's brother, you knew that Nelson couldn't swim. Correct?" said Mr. Hogan.

"Yes," Mervin replied.

"Can you remember ever seeing him in the water?" asked Mr. Hogan.

"Never."

"Was he afraid of the water?" asked Nelson's lawyer.

"So far as I knew he was," replied Mervin.

"Did you have any concerns that the children might be physically abused by Jennifer and Nelson?"

"No."

Jennifer felt relieved when the lawyers said they were finished questioning Mervin. She knew the pressure he faced from his family.

Next it was Jennifer's family who would take the stand. Her brother-in-law Winston finished taking his oath and sat in the box. Mr. Linehan wanted to know about a visit they'd had back in the spring before the girls' deaths. Nelson had to go to St. John's, and that night there was a conversation the Crown was particularly interested in.

"What came up that night during this conversation?" Mr. Linehan asked.

"We were talking about some stuff, and I think we were talking about the kids. I said if somebody was ever to take my kids it would be a hard thing. Nelson said, yes, if somebody ever took mine, you know, I'd probably do away with them."

"His comment, again, to the best of your recollection, was what?" Mr. Linehan asked.

Winston shifted in his seat. "I would make away with them before I let someone take them."

99

Jennifer could already hear Nelson's mother when she woke up at six thirty in the morning. She was on the phone, and she was mad.

This week had already been exhausting enough. Yesterday she had listened to the doctors who worked on Karen and Krista, as well as the medical examiners.

Today she felt like just getting up and walking to the graveyard to be with her girls. But instead, today would be her turn to take the stand.

She thought the shower would make her feel better, but she would have no such luck this morning. Jennifer had never felt so heavy, or so burdened.

At breakfast, Jennifer was subject to pleas to continue to defend Nelson and to do her best on the stand, but Jennifer knew this would be difficult. Jennifer didn't have the energy to listen.

There were things she didn't remember, and things she didn't understand.

She got dressed and headed to the courthouse. The reporters were there, and there were a few extra members of the public. Jennifer figured a lot of people were interested in what she would have to say.

She made her way to the front of the courtroom and sat in the witness box. Other than the lawyers, Nelson was the closest person to her. They were face to face.

"Mrs. Hart, are you currently married?" asked the Crown.

"Yes, to Nelson Hart," she replied. "We've been married now seven years."

Jennifer knew her voice was shaky, especially when the court kept reminding her to speak up so everyone in the jury could hear. A clerk came forward and adjusted her microphone.

"Did you have any children?" he asked.

"Yes, two girls, twin girls. Karen and Krista," she told the court.

"Tell us everything you can remember about the day your daughters died."

"There's not much I can remember," she said. "It's been almost five years now. I got up for breakfast, bathed them, and I got them all dressed because there was a derby that day. Nelson was ready, and they wanted to go to the swings. New swings, they were saying. Nelson said how long are you going to be, and I said about forty-five minutes to an hour. So Nelson took the girls."

"How long was he gone?" asked Mr. Linehan.

"I'd say about half an hour or forty-five minutes, he was gone. He came into the house all in a panic. He was saying, 'Krista's in the water.' I asked him where Karen was, and I guess in the fright he said, 'Karen's down in the car.' But when I got down there, Karen wasn't in the car. I asked him where's Karen, and he said he left her down there."

Jennifer continued on with her testimony, describing the moment she saw Krista in the water. She even managed to show them on a map where the body was. But with each question, it was getting more and more difficult to keep from bursting into tears.

When the questions began about being with Krista at the Janeway, she couldn't hold back anymore.

"I'm going to have to take a break," she said.

After the break, the questioning turned to Nelson and his seizures. The court wanted to know whether Nelson had taken his seizure medication on the day the girls drowned. She said he had because she had given it to him.

Then there were questions about her brother-in-law Mervin and the day she and the social worker called him to see if they could stay there. They had been in the car with the girls and nowhere to live. Jennifer remembered it well.

"I needed a room over the girls' heads. I couldn't have them on the street," she said.

"How did Nelson feel about going to Mervin's?"

"He didn't want me and the girls to go," she replied.

Then came the endless probe into the details of Mr. Big. The court wanted to know everything about her involvement, and she tried her best to remember the details.

"Pat and Carol were going to be married," Jennifer explained. "And where me and Nelson only got married here in the court, we were going to have a double wedding. Nelson was going to get rings for me with diamonds and stuff."

"Let's get back to August 4," the Crown asked. "Did he say how Krista ended up in the water?"

"He said he had a seizure. He said that when I got down to Little Harbour. He said he had one of the small ones. Petit mal, not grand mal."

Mr. Linehan approached her with a document. It was the statement she had given to the police on the day the girls' died.

"In your statement, did you mention anything about a seizure?" he asked.

"No."

"But in a later statement you mentioned he had a seizure, or that something else happened," said Mr. Linehan.

"I heard it somewhere along the line that he said that he had a seizure," she responded.

When questioned, Jennifer couldn't answer where she had first heard Nelson had had a seizure.

"Was it that same day, a day later, or a month later?"

"I wouldn't be able to tell you," she said.

"Can you give us any idea of when you heard of the seizure for the first time?" he pressed on.

"Well, after I came back from PEI is when I found out he came to the police and told them he had a seizure. That was after the girls' deaths. I came back in December."

"So he told you that he didn't tell them about the seizure because he'd lose his driver's licence?"

"Yes," she said.

Jennifer was relieved when one of the jurors was called outside the courtroom. She was happy to get a break from the questioning. There were things she couldn't remember, and she had never felt so confused.

But as soon as the break was over, it was time for the cross-examination by Nelson's lawyer, Derek Hogan.

He went back to December of 2002. Jennifer and Nelson were both being interviewed by the police. Mr. Hogan brought forward Nelson's statement from the interview. *"Remember that day you was in doing your hair, and I stood up by the side, you turned in to the wall. I wanted to tell you I got sick. You know, out there. And I said if I tells her she will probably go hysterical."*

This was the first time he had told Jennifer about the seizure.

"I can recall somewhere along the line that he told me he got sick," said Jennifer.

Jennifer struggled to answer the question until, finally, Mr. Hogan excused her from the stand.

She went back to her seat next to Nelson's mother. She was glad to have it over with, but she couldn't figure out how any of those questions had anything to do with whether or not her husband had killed her two daughters. She hoped she hadn't said anything that was going to make Nelson's mother mad. She was exhausted and in no mood for an argument.

"Yes, My Lord, the next witness for the Crown is Pearl Hart."

"Do you have any children?" asked Mr. Linehan.

"I've got three sons: Nelson Hart, Mervin Hart, and Stephen Hart. Nelson is the oldest, Stephen the youngest."

The Crown went on to ask Nelson's mother about her relationship with Nelson after he and Jennifer had moved back from PEI, two months prior to the girls' deaths. They went from talking every day to no contact at all, and the Crown wanted to know why.

"He came back empty-handed," Pearl explained. "When he arrived he came to me. He was trying to get accommodations for him, Jennifer, and the children."

"And how did that conversation go?" asked Mr. Linehan.

"Well, because of a past incident, I was told that Nelson (I'm sharing a place with a common-law husband) was not to come. I told Nelson that Eric wasn't in favour of him coming," she explained.

"How did he take that news?"

"He responded by being very disappointed," Pearl continued. "He said he was stuck. And I said to him at that time I had a fear, too, as well as Eric. It was because of the problem I've had before with getting help for Nelson from social services. I was afraid that, if I took him and his wife and children, that social services would deny him an apartment in the future. And I couldn't accommodate four people."

"How did Nelson react?"

"Nelson was upset," she said. "He said, 'Mom, I can't believe it. Your own son, you won't take him in.' I tried to explain my fear, and he reminded me that when he did get things straightened out not to come and see the girls, I wouldn't see them because he wouldn't let me in. Which was exactly what he did do."

Pearl went on to tell everyone in the courtroom that for a couple of days she was driving around looking for them. She was concerned for the children, so she contacted social services.

"I contacted them to see why Nelson was denied an apartment," she said. "They said if Nelson doesn't have anywhere to go, the kids will be taken from them. I told them those kids will never go out into a foster home."

Jennifer watched as Pearl continued on. Linehan suggested that she take a break.

"Those kids weren't going out in a foster home. I loved them too much for that," she explained. "And because I was working, and couldn't take them, I contacted my son Mervin. He was well able to provide for them."

"What was Nelson's reaction?"

"Well, he wasn't happy about it," said Pearl.

The attorney went on to ask her about Nelson's new job and his reluctance to talk about his work.

"He said he got it on the Internet," she said. "I found that hard to believe, because Nelson hardly knows what a computer looks like." Though he didn't talk about his work, Pearl noticed he was dressing better and looking good.

Next it was Derek Hogan's turn. Jennifer looked on anxiously.

Nelson had been diagnosed with epilepsy when he was nine months old.

"Would it be accurate to say that you became over-protective of him?"

"Yes, I did," said Pearl. "Nelson . . . it was a fight from day one. Financially. To get help for him. Any time I ever contacted social services for help, I was told that we made too much money. I was encouraged to quit work. Then they would look out to him a hundred per cent. I didn't want to go on welfare, I was looking for help for my child. There were months Nelson cost us a thousand dollars.

Pearl continued to explain the expensive trips to St. John's he required for doctors' appointments. And though they were never hungry, there were sacrifices because of his seizures. There were times he didn't even get a birthday gift.

"Were there times when you thought Nelson shouldn't be alone with the children?" asked Mr. Hogan.

"I was always uneasy of him being alone with the kids, because of his epilepsy," Pearl explained.

She went on to describe the various seizures Nelson had. There were three types varying in severity.

"Did he tell you that he had a seizure on August 4, 2002?" the lawyer asked.

"He told me he didn't have one."

"Sometime later did he tell you?"

"Yes. I don't know, exactly. I think it was about a month and a half or something," Pearl answered. "He sat down in the kitchen one day and started to cry. It wasn't surprising to me, because I had seen him do that a couple of times. He said, 'Mom, I got something to tell ya.' He said he had a seizure down there that day."

Pearl told the courtroom she had thought Nelson might have had a seizure when the girls drowned, but she didn't want to press him. She was the one who phoned the police, and Nelson explained that he wanted to change his story. She said Nelson had always tried to hide his seizures.

"What grade did Nelson go to in school?"

"Five. He did grade five. For three years."

100

The next person to take the stand was an RCMP officer, Cpl. Phil Matthews.

Jennifer thought she could feel Nelson's mother tense up as they listened to him explain the sting operation that would lead to Nelson's arrest.

"The first phase of the traditional investigation had been conducted in the summer of 2004," he said. "For the lack of a better term, it had bottomed out."

That's when the talk of an undercover operation began. Cst. Dave Chubbs had transferred to Gander in the spring of 2004, and he had previously worked in an undercover homicide unit in British Columbia. With Chubbs being available, it was the opportune time to start.

In the fall, they began the process of submitting an operation plan in order to get authorization.

"We anticipated we would need ninety days to run the plan, and we sought $173,575," said Cpl. Matthews.

By late November they had their approval. But things wouldn't go as planned.

Instead of taking ninety days, the operation was going to take longer. In mid-April, they requested an additional $148,837.

Cpl. Matthews said that in April, after playing out thirty-three scenarios, they expected they would need another twenty-seven scenarios in order to obtain a confession from Nelson. Specifically because Nelson was paranoid.

"We didn't realize that we were going to have to move the operation from Newfoundland to the Montreal and Halifax area," he told the court. "It was getting too problematic to continue running the program in Newfoundland, because it is so small and there are so many policemen."

The operation ended up costing $413,268.

101

For an entire week, Jennifer sat in shock. She listened to both Pat and Steph recall the months they had spent with Nelson.

Nelson had thought they were his friends. He thought he had a good job. Instead, the police had lured him in. As she looked between Nelson and his former friends, she felt sad for her husband.

She was stunned as she listened to the details. Nelson was travelling all over the mainland. And then there was the money. While he was hiding $20 bills around the house, he was getting paid thousands.

But through her anger, Nelson's mother was there to reassure her. Nelson had been tricked. It was all a lie. A lie with a goal of obtaining a false confession, in her view.

But Jennifer trembled with fear on this Thursday morning. A videotape had been loaded into the machine at the front of the courtroom, and Jennifer was worried about what she was preparing to watch.

A man named Sgt. Haslett was on the stand, and he described what they saw on the screen.

"That's the picture of the hotel room that we were in. It's obviously a smaller couch and one chair there. The drapes are closed," he stated.

The man who was on the stand was also on the screen. He's walking back and forth and speaking on the phone. Steph is sitting on the couch. Nelson comes into the frame.

Jennifer struggled to hear the conversation on the tape. She listened as Nelson told the man in the other chair that he hadn't hurt his daughters. But his words rang in her ears when he admitted to killing them.

She couldn't take any more. All she wanted to do was run to the front of the court, grab Nelson, and haul him to the floor. She ran from the courtroom as quickly as she could. As she bolted through the courtroom doors, she was aware of someone following her.

She felt an arm around her shoulder, and she recognized the woman from victim services who had been sitting in the courtroom.

She led her down the hallway into a small office. Jennifer couldn't stop crying. The woman handed her a box of tissues.

"Jennifer, are you sure you don't want to do a victim impact statement, so you can tell the court how you feel about everything that's happened?" she asked.

Jennifer had no idea what she was talking about, and she didn't care. She wasn't giving the court anything.

Jennifer stayed in the office until she felt strong enough to face the courtroom again. Especially Nelson's mother. In her heart, Jennifer was afraid that Nelson had killed the girls. Why else had he said he had something in the back of his mind he would take to the grave? Why did he tell that man he did it? But before Jennifer could think about anything else, Nelson's mother was by her side.

"Don't you worry. They trapped him into saying that."

Jennifer no longer had the energy to talk about it. She just wanted to go home.

102

"Is Nelson going to testify?" Jennifer asked Nelson's mother.

"He's afraid he's going to have a seizure. He'll do it, but not in front of the courtroom. You know how nervous he gets in front of a crowd. He'll probably have a seizure for sure."

Judge Wayne Diamond had actually offered Nelson a screen to block out the crowd. He had also offered to have a doctor present in the courtroom while Nelson testified. But the judge wasn't about to let him testify in private, because he had lied about his seizures in the past to get more money from social services. He'd also lied about seizures to keep his driver's licence.

In the end, Nelson didn't want to testify.

But Jennifer believed there was another reason he didn't want to testify. She believed he wouldn't be able to lie in front of a big crowd. She also believed he was afraid that people would see through his story.

103

Guilty.

Jennifer couldn't believe it. She started to shake. All she wanted to do was run from this place. And that is exactly what she did. She ran out into the lobby so she could shed her tears in peace. Now, more than ever, she was convinced that Nelson's mother was right. There was no way he could have ever done this.

A few minutes later and the crowd began to pour out of the courtroom. Jennifer couldn't remember ever seeing Nelson's mother so mad. And so was she. What if they had set Nelson up? Now he would go to prison for an automatic life sentence of twenty-five years.

Nelson's mother reached out to her, and together they retreated to an office.

"This is not fair," Jennifer cried. "He didn't do this."

One of the clerks opened the door. "It's time to go back in," she said.

Inside the courtroom, Nelson was preparing to say a few words.

"I was told not to go against the crime boss," he said. "I tried to tell him the truth, but he didn't believe that."

Jennifer was exhausted. As the crowd began to leave the courtroom, she followed.

Outside, a crowd of reporters were interviewing Nelson's

lawyer. They waited until the interview was over and then went outside. Jennifer had nothing to say to the cameras and microphones, but Nelson's mother had plenty to say.

"There's a lot about this story that's not right," she said. "My son faces a grim future behind bars."

Jennifer already knew that his mother was going to be fighting the decision all the way. Nelson's lawyer made it clear they would be appealing.

His mother continued to make her case in front of the reporters as Jennifer listened in.

Finally, the questions came to an end, and she was relieved to be sitting in the quiet of the car. Except Nelson's mother wasn't going to be quiet about this verdict at all. All the way home, she talked about how they would fight to have him released from jail.

Jennifer went back to Mrs. Hart's, and for the rest of the night she listened to the endless phone calls and questions from people who had watched the results of the trial on the evening news. Nelson's mother had the same story for each of them. Her son was innocent and she was going to put things straight.

Even though she had never felt so exhausted in her life, there was no sleep at all for Jennifer that night.

104

The next morning, Nelson's mother made breakfast for Jennifer. But each bite of toast was nearly impossible to swallow.

"I just need to go home right now and get things straightened out." But all she really wanted was to be alone. She was tired of talking about Nelson, tired of listening to the constant ranting about him being framed.

Even though Jennifer had stood by Nelson and his mother throughout the trial, there was still a part of her that questioned whether or not Nelson was guilty. She quickly put the thought out of her mind, packed her bags, and headed for home.

Everything seemed different to her this morning. She felt like her ears were ringing from the weeks of being in the courtroom and listening to her mother-in-law. And as soon as things were quiet, she began questioning the voices she was hearing in her own head. By the time she made it halfway home, she had a splitting headache.

When she finally got back to the apartment, she went straight to the cupboard to grab a couple of Tylenol, and then she lay down. At this moment she didn't care if she ever moved again.

Jennifer had missed having a telephone at the apartment, but right now she was glad no one could reach her. She knew the media from right across the country were trying to find her, and she certainly had no interest in hearing from Nelson right now.

Two days after the sentencing, he had been transferred to the penitentiary in St. John's, and Jennifer knew he was having a hard time. He claimed the guards didn't like him there.

As much as she pitied him for everything he was going through inside, Jennifer was battling her own demons.

Then there were the lawyers. He believed the legal aid lawyers weren't capable of representing him from day one. Halfway through the trial, he even talked about firing Mr. Hogan. Jennifer didn't know which lawyer would end up fighting the appeal, but she had spent enough time thinking about the trial for now.

For two full weeks she didn't leave the apartment, until one morning she woke up and knew something wasn't right.

As she made her way to the bathroom, she got dizzy. So light-headed, in fact, she had to sit on the floor. Then her world went dark to the extent she wondered if she was going blind. But with no one around to help her, she had to wait out the symptoms until she felt well enough to go the doctor.

"It looks like you've had a mini-stroke," he told her. "No doubt, Jennifer, you've been under a lot of pressure, and you're going to have to start relaxing. If not, you could very well end up back here with a much more severe stroke."

105

As the weeks turned into months, there were fewer trips to see the Harts.

Nelson had become agitated, and fighting the appeal was nearly impossible because he wanted to change lawyers every time progress was made. Each time Nelson demanded a new lawyer, his mother went to work to try and help him.

But Jennifer was finding him more difficult to deal with these days. He was accusing her of working for the police. He believed she was trying to get information against him, and he even started refusing the money she was sending to him. He told her the guards were giving him a hard time, and he believed they had bugged his cell.

He was angry, and Jennifer couldn't take much more. She was expecting any day he would kill himself.

With Nelson's unstable mental condition, an effort was put under way to give Jennifer power of attorney. But she no longer wanted anything to do with his appeal. The more time passed, the more she was convinced he was guilty.

Since the sentencing, she had found it increasingly difficult to be so far away from the girls. As soon as Nelson returned to prison, she moved back to Gander to be closer to them. And just as her life began to settle, she got another call that would change things forever.

"Jennifer, it's Dad," said Penny. "He . . . it happened this morning."

Jennifer had known her father was complaining about

feeling sick all week, but there was no way to prepare for the shocking news.

When she thought there were no tears left to cry, Jennifer began to cry and struggled to hang on to the receiver.

Her father had been suffering gallbladder problems, and he was supposed to have surgery to have it removed. However, he cancelled the appointment, thinking it would go away on its own. But his gallbladder had been on the verge of rupturing all along.

"He got up this morning and had two spoonfuls of soup and a slice of bread," Penny explained. "Then he went back to bed, and the next thing we knew he was gone."

106

At the same time Jennifer lost her father, another man came into her life. It was a taxi driver named Scott, who gave Jennifer hope that she could go back to having a normal, happy life.

The two of them hit it off right away, and their friendship soon turned to a relationship. After the years of struggling with Nelson, she had never realized someone could treat her so well.

When she suffered a back injury, he was there whenever he had a break. He fixed her meals and helped her with the simplest of chores. With the injury, it was difficult just getting out of bed. He brought her to visit the girls' graves, sometimes without her even needing to ask.

But her happiness failed to last once again.

On the morning of September 30, 2011, Scott had left Jennifer's to deliver a package to the hospital. She went about her business of getting ready that morning until she faced the police officer standing in the apartment door.

Scott had been killed in a serious car accident.

Jennifer slowly began picking up the pieces again, but she wanted Nelson out of her life for good.

In 2012, she went to the courthouse to get a divorce. However, Nelson wouldn't sign, so special procedures had to be followed. Two weeks after the process began, the divorce was finalized.

AFTERWORD

In August 2014, the Supreme Court of Canada decided the Mr. Big operation used to obtain Nelson Hart's confession was unreliable and inadmissible.

The Crown withdrew the charge of murder, and Nelson Hart was released from prison in Bishop's Falls.

Nelson Hart's lawyers called the sting operation the perfect storm. There was psychological manipulation by the police, and Mr. Hart was an extremely vulnerable target, according to defence lawyer Robby Ash.

Nelson served a total of nine years in prison. There is no word on whether there will be a wrongful prosecution suit from the lawyers, but his mother says there's no question they will be seeking compensation for wrongful conviction.

Jennifer Hicks lives with her fiancé in Gander. While she's come a long way financially and emotionally, she wishes her daughters could be here to be part of this new life.

The investigation into the deaths of Karen and Krista Hart could potentially be reopened should the police find additional evidence. Jennifer is holding on to that hope.

"I had to fight for my youngsters ever since they came into the world. From the first hour they were born. I am still fighting for them."

Today Jennifer spends as much time as she can at the Salvation Army Cemetery in Gander. The pain is still as sharp today as it was in 2002. Photo by Colleen Lewis.

Gander Lake as it is today. The old wharf where Karen and Krista drowned has since been removed, but these pictures were taken from the area where the drownings occurred. Photos by Colleen Lewis.

COMMENTARY WRITTEN BY JENNIFER HICKS

I am so saddened that Nelson has gotten out of prison. My life has been turned upside down. Why should he be out and happy while I'm suffering all my life without my precious angels? When they died, I died.

When they were born, I thought I had the world, I knew I had it in the palm of my hand. They were my life. I look at people with their families and it hurts. Why couldn't Nelson be a good father? If he were half the father I was a mother, the girls would still be with me. March 9, 2015, would have been their sixteenth birthday, and I couldn't even give them their daughters' pride rings.

I shouldn't have to go through this. I should be able to enjoy my girls, watch them grow up, go to school, and get married. I wanted to be a grandmother, but that will never happen because of Nelson Hart.

I often find myself down at the gravesite. I've been doing that ever since they passed away. I would give anything to have them walk through my door and say, "Mommy, I'm home." There are days I go down to where my angels are and it's okay. But more times, I don't want to leave.

Nelson needs to pay for what he did to my girls and me. I won't stop until I get justice.

ACKNOWLEDGEMENTS

Many thanks to Flanker Press and Jerry, Garry, and Margo Cranford for their help, professionalism, and dedication.

This book could never have happened without the continued courage from Jennifer Hicks, who so often struggled to relive the most difficult moments a parent could ever imagine.

To Marissa, who went to bed a little earlier each night so Mommy could write, I love you.

Colleen Lewis spent her early years in Rocky Harbour and grew up in Deer Lake. She spent several years as a print reporter, and for the past twelve years she has been a video journalist with NTV.

She followed the story of Karen and Krista Hart since the arrest of their father, Nelson Hart, until the summer of 2014, when he was released.

Jennifer Lisa Hicks was born to Gertrude and Cyril Hicks of Musgrave Harbour, Newfoundland and Labrador, in 1974. She went to Gill Memorial Academy for a few years before attending elementary school and Lester Pearson High School.

She started working at the Good Luck Restaurant in Valleyfield, Bonavista Bay, until she moved to Gander in 1997, where she began post-secondary education in business administration at the Career Academy. While in Gander, she began working at the Albatross Hotel.

In October 1997, Jennifer met and moved in with Nelson Hart, and soon after that she became a full-time mom. Her daughters, Karen and Krista, were born in March 1999. Jennifer's life was turned upside down in 2002 when she lost the two most important people in her life, her precious daughters.

Today, Jennifer has a fiancé, Myles Gunn. Her life is better now, but it will never be the same without the two daughters she misses dearly.

Visit Flanker Press at:

www.flankerpress.com

https://www.facebook.com/flankerpress

https://twitter.com/FlankerPress

http://www.youtube.com/user/FlankerPress